THE MAKING OF A SPIRITUAL MEDIUM

BY

YVONNE BAILEY

To Kelly my new neighbour.

With love

Yvonne xx

Conditions of sale

This book is sold subject to the condition that it shall not, by way of trade or otherwise, be lent, re-sold, hired out or otherwise circulated in any form of binding or cover other than that in which it is published and without a similar condition including this condition being imposed on the subsequent purchaser.

First published in Great Britain by
Spiritworldonline Ltd
9 Barquentine Place
Atlantic Wharf
Cardiff
CF10 4NF

http://www.spiritworldonline.com

A CIP record for this book is available from the British Library.

ISBN 0-9550612-0-2

Printed and bound in Great Britain by Creative Print and Design Wales, Ebbw Vale.

This semi-autobiographical novel is a book about spirit communication and personal growth. It is written to help those who are focusing on self-development and are walking the spiritual path. More importantly, it should be of immense help to those who are being dragged, kicking and screaming along the path. It is an example of a spiritual journey. It is part my story, part your story and part any ones story.

Disclaimer

People and events have been changed to protect the innocent and any similarities to actual persons, either living or dead, are merely coincidental.

Yvonne is presently working on 'Yvonne Bailey's Book of Symbols and Dreams'.

This should be ready shortly and she is taking orders now.

You can contact Yvonne by visiting http://www.spiritworldonline.com or writing to:

Spiritworldonline Ltd.,
9 Barquentine Place
Atlantic Wharf
Cardiff
CF10 4NF

This book is dedicated to my parents, Berit and Vivian Bailey, for all the love they have shown me.

Also to my son, Kristian Bailey, for his unwavering support and belief in me.

Also to my sister Gail, my niece Tracy and my great-niece Sophia, for enriching my life.

To all of my family, both on earth and in spirit, with much love.

Yve xx

Contents

One

The Plan

There is a plan to our life on earth. Our date of birth is chosen as the planets are an energy influence, and this influence contributes to our character traits. Our parents are chosen for the genes we will inherit and the environment we will live in.

Cardiff is the capital city of Wales. In the nineteenth century it had the busiest sea port in the world, because of the thriving coal and iron trades. On the eve of the First World War in 1913, coal exports reached their peak and the international price of coal was struck in the Coal Exchange building in the dockland area. It was here that the world's first one million pound deal was signed. Eventually that one million pound cheque was framed, and as far as I am aware, still hangs in the Coal Exchange building.

To sustain this growth the surrounding docklands areas grew into cosmopolitan communities, with seafarers from all around the world making Cardiff their home, and the dockland area known as 'Tiger Bay' achieving world wide fame. My father Vivian was born and lived in Splott, the youngest of four boys. The area of Splott is next to the Docklands.

It is a very different story now in Cardiff, as after the Second World War demand for coal slumped and international markets were lost as other countries developed their own steel industries. By the 1960s coal exports had virtually ceased. Cardiff has had to totally reinvent itself and has done so very successfully, attracting foreign investment and relying heavily on the service industries, especially tourism.

The Bay where I live is on the site of the old docks, spreading out in to the docks' community. Appealing apartments and houses are intermingled with a brilliant mix of restaurants, pubs, clubs, cinema, bowling, a casino, the exciting Millennium Arts Centre and fantastic places of historic interest including the Norwegian Church, which has a special place in my heart. This is all set around our wonderful harbour. A barrage has been put in place, as we have one of the world's greatest tidal ranges up to fourteen meters. At low tide our harbour would have been inaccessible for up to fourteen hours a day. The barrage eliminates the effects of the tide, and gives Cardiff the opportunity to once again capitalise on its greatest asset – its waterfront.

My mother's father was a Norwegian seaman. His name was Bjorn Kristian Kjonnings and he was a Chief Engineer. When his ship sailed into Cardiff Docks in 1920 it would have been a different docklands that greeted him. He met my mother's mum, Beatrice, when walking around Cardiff Castle. At that time he could hardly speak English. Beatrice married her Norwegian seaman and they had four daughters, but he died at the age of fifty-three. My mother was the third of their four girls. Her name is Berit, and she and her youngest sister Maureen both married local men, the older two sisters having married and moved away. My Aunty Maureen's husband was named Emrys, and together they had four children. My parents had two children, me and my sister Gail.

My name is Yvonne and I was born in 1953 in my grandmother Beatty's house on a council estate in Tremorfa, which is an area next to Splott. In that house lived my grandmother, mother, father, sister and me, plus Maureen and Emrys, all in a three bedroomed house!

In 1955 my mum and dad were given a new council house in Llanrumney, to the East of Cardiff. Maureen and Emrys stayed with my grandmother, and raised their eventual family with her help.

My father and Uncle Emrys both worked in the Eastmoors Steelworks and our households were very close. My dad worked in the melting shop, and sometimes the skin on his back would be red and sore because of lime dust. I never heard him complain, and he worked all the hours he could to ensure we had a nice home.

In the early days of our moving he relied on public transport to take him back and forth to the steelworks in Splott. I know there were occasions when the transport wasn't running due to bad weather, and my dad would walk to work and back, even if there were thick snow. This was a round trip of about ten miles, with two very steep hills to climb. He worked Christmas days and Boxing days; he was no stranger to doublers, sixteen hour shifts, so he could provide for us.

My mother had the best of everything. She loved clothes, and my father bought her a long fur coat. She wore high heeled shoes, and I used to think she looked like a film star. My mum made all the clothes for us two girls and was a perfectionist, very conscious of our image to the outside world.

In the early days our mum was a housewife, later taking a part-time job as a waitress. I can clearly remember that two bedroomed house. We were a happy household, and my parents bought a German shepherd dog we named Pal, and so we were a family of five. We were two streets away from a farm and my sister and I, along with neighbour's children, would go to the farm and look at the animals. Sometimes the farmer would let us help and that was magic. We always had Pal trailing behind us.

From small children my sister and I were sent to Sunday school at the local Methodist Church. I loved the Bible stories and really believed all I was taught. God became a big part of my life. If I was anxious or frightened about anything, I would pray to God and do deals with him. I was particularly anxious about my father. My mother would often refer to him as 'your poor father' and point out to my sister and me all the hard work and sacrifices he made for our family. My mum made me feel so sorry for him.

My dad had a clever mind, and could have really achieved academically. He was born in 1927 and as a boy he went to Moorland Road School in Splott. He won a place at a grammar school, but my grandmother reasoned her other three boys hadn't had this opportunity, so it wasn't right my dad should. His Headmaster from the School went to see my nan at home, but she was not for turning. My dad missed a wonderful opportunity, but he never resented it.

My dad left school at fourteen and went to work on the railways. He started as a cleaner in the engine shed, but quickly became a locomotive fireman. In 1946 at the age of eighteen he volunteered for the Army, and was sent to Palestine with the 21st Lancers. He was in the army for six years, during which time he married my mother, and my sister Gail was born. When he left the army his rank was a Corporal, and he was a Gunnery Instructor on Centurion Tanks. He loved his job but my mother didn't want the life of an army wife, and gave him an ultimatum. This is how he came to work in the steelworks.

My dad was a very passionate man; he loved my mum and us kids fiercely. He was very involved with the Union in the steelworks, and was a staunch believer in fighting for workers' rights. He would sit on industrial tribunals, and I used to listen to his tales of injustice against workers. He was a charismatic speaker, but had a fiery temper, and could look really frightening when in a rage. He loved animals and would take Pal for long walks in the countryside when he came home from his shift. If he was on the night shift my mother would say, 'your poor father has worked all night'. And my sister and I would have to be quiet around the house as my 'poor father' would be sleeping.

My first spiritual experience took place when I was about four. At night I would come out of my body. I don't remember how this happened or where I went, but I remember the coming back. I would have a man with me, who I now recognise as my spirit guide HQ. I would tell him I didn't want to go back into my body; I wanted to go into someone else's body just to see what it was like. He would always answer, 'I have told you before, this is your body and this is where you belong, you cannot enter someone else's body'.

I remember that when I would wake in the morning, I would feel very guilty because I had been disloyal to my parents by wanting to be someone else for a while. I imagine it was this that stopped me confiding the experience.

My mum was born in 1929 and had the potential to be a medium. From a child she had spiritual experiences but was terrified of them. My sister and I grew up with the stories of how, when my mother was little, she would see faces on her eyelids when she closed her eyes at night. They were of no one she knew and would mouth words that she couldn't understand. Sometimes the faces were distorted. She would be so frightened she wouldn't go to sleep.

My mum has been an asthmatic all her life and as a child was very frail, her episodes of seeing were called hallucinations by the Doctor. Sometimes my mum would see faces when her eyes were open. They could be on the wall, in a corner, anywhere and she would scream. My poor nan must have been frazzled with it. I can vividly remember sitting at the table with my mum and she would be motionless, just staring ahead. My sister and I would ask her to 'stop it' but she didn't seem able. My mum also had problems sleeping, and was horrified to experience sleep paralysis. She would wake up from sleep and be unable to move. She couldn't open her eyes or her mouth, and was unable to make a noise. This terrified her.

At one stage my mother was seeing a psychiatrist to help her with these problems. If only she could have gone to an experienced medium to help her understand what was happening to her, but there was no one to turn too, just the medical profession. My mum is seventy-six now and still sees the faces on her eyelids. She still sits staring into space, but is no longer afraid.

My mum was incredibly close to her mother and her sister Maureen, and I think it was quite a hardship for her to move away from them. When my father was in work, my mother would take my sister and me back and forth to Tremorfa on the bus, so we could visit with my nan and the others. Very often we would sit, and the adults would talk about spiritual matters. My cousins, sister and me would be fascinated to hear of these happenings. They talked of when our nan's brother was in hospital, but he appeared at the house, knocking on the front door moments before they were given the news he had died. They said when our gramp died, later that night he could be heard walking up the stairs in the house. Apparently my nan's sister Maggie was into spiritual things, and could read tea leaves. They would also talk about neighbours, with my mother catching up on the local gossip. There was such a diversity of people, all working class, most struggling to provide for their families.

My parents would try to have one night out a week with my aunt and uncle, and we kids would be looked after by our nana Beatty at her house. Very often the drink would cause arguments, and on their return my father would over react and my sister and I would be crying and frightened. In the mornings my mother would say 'Your poor father, he is so upset about last night', and I would feel desperately sorry for my 'poor father'.

My mother did eventually settle in Llanrumney, as our new area was made up of young families with children, and mum made friends with most of the other mothers. Across the road lived Peggy and Arthur with their son Russell, and Peggy became my mother's lifelong friend, until Peggy's death three years ago.

7

My mum and dad grew up in the war years, and I think their generation had a need for security that perhaps made them cautious of life. My parents had negative opinions about most things outside of their environment. They are both forceful and controlling personalities, as well as being very loving, and over-protective of my sister and me. My dad is a strong Leo, my mother a fiery Aries, and my sister and I are both nurturing Cancerians.

My mother would control in an emotional way, which was how her own mother had been. If my dad was on night shift, sometimes my sister and I would play her up and be naughty when in bed at night. My mum would shout up to us 'If you don't behave I am going to run away'. Sometimes she would pretend she was leaving, and would make exaggerated walking noises, and then slam the front door. My sister and I would listen and then start to cry. My mum would say 'Right, I am giving you one more chance'. At other times she would say 'I'm going to run to the tide fields and drown myself if you don't go to sleep' and again she might make exaggerated walking noises and slam the front door.

My mum was the leader of our little pack, and would normally get the better of my father. When my dad would leave for his shift I would pray to God to bring him home safely, and would always negotiate some deal or other, what I would do for God if he looked after my 'poor father'. Some days I would avoid walking on cracks on the pavement, another I might compulsively count certain things. I still do the counting thing to this day, and sometimes it is worse than others. It can be really intrusive.

I used to worry about religion a lot, there seemed so many rules and regulations, and God was portrayed as a very judgemental person. If I met anyone who was really nice but wasn't a Christian, I would worry about them, thinking what would happen to them when they died. My prayers at night used to take for ever, the list of people to be included got longer and longer, and then I would compulsively worry that I had forgotten someone and would run through a quick check list.

My mother used to use the Bible if there was any conflict. She would get the Bible out and ask my sister and me to swear on the Bible, this was a means of ensuring she had the truth from us. One time cream had been taken from the fridge. My sister swore on the Bible it wasn't her. My parents were exempt from such matters, so that left me. I hadn't taken the cream, but I reasoned if I swore on the Bible I hadn't taken the cream, something bad must surely happen. Someone in our family was lying, or if they weren't lying, then I must have taken the cream and not remembered. I did a quick negotiation in my mind with God and took the blame.

Having said all this I know I was a very sunny child, always talking, laughing and singing. The anxiety and worries were for me alone to know. I am positive I never shared this part of me with anyone else. I was also a very emotional child, and when I was taken to watch Bambi in the cinema I cried so much I was hyperventilating. Anything remotely sad would have me in floods of tears.

My mother's health continued to be a problem. Her asthma was very bad. My mother later told us of a wonderful spiritual experience she had at a time when she was particularly poorly with pneumonia. My mum had been terribly ill in the night, and my father was working nights. In those days if you didn't work you got no pay. He had to go to work, but worried all night and came home at seven in the morning. He got my sister and me ready, and left my mum in the house whilst he walked us to school. He then telephoned the Doctor from a telephone kiosk.

In the meantime my mother was in bed and, as ill as she was, felt impressed to get out of bed and practically crawled to the back bedroom. She laid on the bed and sun streamed through the bedroom window. My mum lay there with the sun shining on her, feeling wonderfully warm, and listening to the sound of birds. She could smell fantastic flowers, and she said the feeling was incredible. She felt totally detached from her body, with no pain or worries and the sun, birds and flowers engulfed her, and she was part of them.

My father came home and couldn't believe my mother had left their bed. He asked my mother what she was doing, and my mother told him she was enjoying the warmth of the sun, listening to the birds and smelling the lovely flowers. My father told my mother it was dark, raining and cold outside with not a bird or flower in sight. Shortly after that experience my mother started to feel better.

We were a happy and loving little household, but with imperfections the same as any other household, although ours was to a lesser extent than a lot of others around us. My parents did their very best for us, and when my dad bought a car I can remember lovely holidays. There would be our family in our car, and Maureen and Emrys with their four children in their car, and we would drive to Devon. For one week we would sleep in the cars, and the other week we would be in caravans. In that first week my mother and aunt would cook on primus stoves on the side of the road.

One time, when I was about seven, my parents saved for us to go to a holiday camp. We had such a fantastic time. We were in the ballroom one evening and my parents were dancing. There was a man about the same age as my dad, and he was making a fuss of me. I remember him saying 'I bet you don't know how to get into your chalet without the key' and I said I did. He was teasing me and saying he didn't believe me, and I offered to show him.

I left the ballroom with him, went to our chalet and got in through a very small window. I opened the door in triumph, and the man came in. I didn't expect that, and was very uncomfortable. He closed the door, pulled the curtain closed and laid me on the bed. He lay at the side of me, and started cuddling and kissing me. I didn't like it and struggled. I told him my father would be back at any minute to look for me. He let me go, and I ran to the door. He got off the bed and left.

I closed the chalet and went back to the ballroom, but I felt so awful. I knew something not very nice had happened, and that I was guilty in some way. My parents always took such good care of me and I had let them down. I couldn't tell my father as I think murder would have been committed. I was always frightened of his temper and knew he could be punished by the law if he did anything in a temper.

In our road were about forty houses. A few of these houses had large families, and the home life for some was not good. My parents would tell my sister and me about the 'goings on' in these households, and we would feel very sorry for the children involved.

I remember one time when my mother offered shoes I had grown out of to one of these families. The mother was really grateful and called one of her sons, who was in my class at school, and asked him to try the shoes on. He got them on with difficulty, as they were too small, and he was making a fuss about it. His mother hit him across the head because of this. My mum and I were so upset, and she never offered shoes to that lady again.

In another road near to ours, I had become friendly with a girl who always had a lot of money. I would go to the ice cream van with her, and she would buy both of us masses of stuff. She said her mother's boyfriend gave her the money.

One day she took me to her house. The smell inside was disgusting. I was aware it was very cold in the rooms, with no carpet on the floors and piles of dirty washing everywhere. Upstairs in a bedroom was a baby with a napkin hanging down his legs, heavy with urine. He was covered in excrement that had seeped from his nappy. The smell was vile, and there was no one in the house. The baby was on his own, and really distressed. My friend was not at all fazed by this, but went and got a bottle for the baby. She laid him down, so he could hold it himself.

I didn't know how to express the compassion I felt; it enveloped me like a blanket. From then on I wanted to do nice things for this girl all the time. I couldn't stop thinking about what I had seen and realised how very, very lucky I was. My friend and I would have been about nine years of age at this time.

I loved school, and excelled at drama and singing. There has always been something of an actress about me, and to this day I sing away when I am working. I was also good at English, and loved to write essays. My mother says I was a constant talker, and would even read out loud to myself.

Our lives had a rhythm, everything revolved around the home and our family in Tremorfa. Sometimes we would go to my dad's mum Emily who lived in Splott, and I loved it when I could stay with her for the day. Emily's husband William, my grandfather, died when I was a baby.

I always went to the local library near to where nana Emily lived. The building was really old with highly polished wood and it had a distinctive musty book smell. The hushed atmosphere would make you think there were wonderful secrets in all those books, and this appealed to my sense of drama.

My dad's brother Frank and his wife Phyllis lived around the corner from my nana Emily, and I am not sure how much they appreciated my love of music, for I would bash away at their piano, even though I couldn't play a note.

Life for me was very secure and happy, but living with two dominant parents meant I wasn't forming my own opinions, and I was prone to feeling sorry for people. The God thing was a worry because he was all seeing, and my religion made him seem so judgemental, and so life with all its rules and regulations was a big responsibility. I also had a vague sense of there being something else around me, but that something wasn't tangible and therefore unexplainable.

When I was eleven our wonderful dog Pal died, and the pain I felt was indescribable. We had been on holiday for two weeks, and Pal was put in his regular holiday boarding kennels. We were waiting for the van to appear in the street to bring him home to us. The van came, and the man got out, but Pal wasn't with him. I thought my world had ended.

We had taken a neighbour's daughter with us on that holiday, and unbelievably her father had died while we were away. He was only in his thirties and seemed in perfect health when we left for the holiday. I can remember being with her and I wasn't able to stop crying. She told me her loss was far worse than mine, which of course it was. She was so calm and able to contain her emotions. I recognised this and admired her for the control she showed, whilst I had absolutely none. I think of her sometimes and realise how incredibly brave she was.

That year we also moved house. We were given a transfer to a three bedroomed council house in Tremorfa. My mother's asthma facilitated this for us, as it was recognised the air in Llanrumney was not good for her. She had asthma attacks and chest problems the whole of the time we lived there.

13

I was so sad to leave our little house, our friends and neighbours, and particularly upset to be leaving what was left of our life with Pal. Around that time I had a dream where Pal and I were standing on the top of a hill. I was walking away from him, but he was following me and I was telling him he couldn't come. However, he continued to follow me, and then I woke up. I hoped he was saying he would follow where ever I went.

Our new house was around the corner from my nana and aunt's house, and it was great to be able to go in and out of there, and be with my cousins.

Moving home meant moving school, and as I already had friends in Splott Secondary Modern School, I was really happy about this. The school stood on Splott Road and was in an old Victorian building, with the boys kept separate from the girls. You attended a secondary modern school if you had failed the eleven plus, as this exam supposedly ascertained the type of schooling that was appropriate for you.

I loved that school, although there was a shortage of facilities. For instance, the toilets were in the playground, with the girls backing on to the boys toilets. The boys had knocked a hole through so that the girls couldn't use certain toilets. At lunch time, if you had school dinners you would line up in the yard and be marched down the road to Eastmoors Hall. The dinners were cooked off the premises, and arrived in large steel containers. For field games, we would be marched to Splott Park.

There was such a lot of poverty in that school, and various nationalities attended as pupils. Quite a few of the kids had prostitutes for mums, and there were a lot of absent fathers. Some of the home lives of different children were terrible.

I remember one incident where all the kids were lined up in the morning, waiting to be marched in to school for the day. There was total silence in the playground, and suddenly a male voice rang out, calling the name of one of the girls. The high stone walls that surrounded the school magnified his voice. We all looked, and there was a scruffily dressed man shouting to one of our school friends. Apparently this was her mother's boyfriend, and that morning our friend had taken his shoe laces for her shoes. He made her take off her shoes, undo the laces, and hand them to him in front of all of us. Not a word was said by anyone, the teachers didn't intervene. He swore at her whilst snatching the laces, and she had to walk back to her place with her shoes slapping against the soles of her feet.

I can remember looking at her sad, down-turned face and feeling such overwhelming emotion for her, but not knowing how to express this. You could see the other pupils and the teachers felt the same as I did. She was given her space but treated with kid gloves by all of us.

Another time, one of the boys was in the girls' playground showing off. A male teacher came to march him away and the boy obviously felt embarrassed. He was black, very popular, a bit of a clown, but known for having things bad at home. His clowning turned to aggression and he picked up a metal netball post and swung it at the teacher's head, knocking him to the ground. The teacher was rescued by his colleagues and the boy marched away, and then we never saw him at school again.

One of the girls in our class lived with her mum and brothers and sisters. There was no dad at home. The mum was dying of cancer and all the kids faced the prospect of going into care. Something happened in a cookery lesson which made this girl flip. She hit the cookery teacher, and the teacher ran out to get the headmistress. The headmistress was then attacked. This girl was expelled from the school, but we all knew that she was reacting to overwhelming feelings of grief, and none of us girls wanted her expelled.

Near to our new house was a mother, father and their two teenage daughters. The father had gone to prison for interfering with the daughters and the mother was having a relationship with a much younger man. When the father came out of prison he moved back in with his wife and daughters, and his wife continued the relationship with the younger man. I have seen that younger man jump out of the first floor window because the husband was entering the house.

This younger man used to dress in black leather and he had a motor bike. He used to sometimes pretend to be a policeman and would ride up to a busy junction in his leathers, stand the bike in a prominent position, and direct the traffic. He was prosecuted for this.

One of the daughters left home at fifteen and we never saw her again. The other daughter went on to have about five children by different men. Most of them eventually ended up in care. One of the babies was born blind, and we were told this was the result of the mother having an untreated venereal disease. Another of the babies died at about six weeks, as the mother had him in bed with her and rolled on to him. She was about twenty-stone in weight.

One time at Christmas three of these kids were in the street on Christmas day. They were in their underwear and the eldest was only about five. My mum and a neighbour asked them where their mother and grandparents were, and were told there was no one home. They had been left alone from the day before. The house was cold and there was no sign of any Christmas presents or food. The neighbour took them in and fed them that morning.

Another time I remember seeing men going in to the house with camera equipment. My mother said the mother and daughter were posing for pornographic pictures.

One of my good friends in school was of mixed race. Her mum was white and her father was black. She had quite a few brothers and sisters, and her father sexually abused all of them, including my friend. They lived in fear of him, and I remember my friend used to be withdrawn and so quiet at times. I didn't know then the extent of what was going on in her home life. I only found out later when her father was jailed for attempting to murder her sister.

My last school year was spent at Willows High School in Tremorfa, which was a replacement for the ancient Splott School. It was so exciting to be among the first pupils to use the new facility.

I didn't know anyone that wasn't working class, until one day a teacher at the school took my friend and me home to her house. She drove us there in a sporty car, and genuinely wanted to give us a nice experience. She was such a positive personality and we girls loved her. I can remember her showing us her husband's wardrobes. There were rows upon rows of shirts, all colour coded. Another wardrobe held all his suits, and I couldn't believe it. My friend and I were overwhelmed and didn't touch anything but just soaked it all in.

Our teacher's husband came home unexpectedly, and it was obvious he wasn't pleased to see us there. We had to leave immediately. He gave us a lift in his car, and dropped us off on the main road that runs through Cardiff, about two miles from our home.

We had to walk the rest of the way. That made me feel bad and I couldn't tell my parents where I had been and what the husband did, as my father would have gone ballistic. I could imagine him going to their home and grabbing the husband by the throat. My father was forever giving lifts to me, my sister and our friends so we would be safe, and this man hadn't given a thought to our safety.

At this time I got my first job, working on a Saturday for a delicatessen on Bute Street in the Docks. It was opposite a pub called the Custom House, and all the prostitutes used to use this pub as a meeting place. I would look out of the big window in fascination.

The family I worked for were Greek and I really loved them. They were so kind to me. The smell in the shop was amazing, and I loved the different coloured olives and the fascinating cheeses. The herbs and spices were incredible, and the colour and smell of them was a new experience for me.

The customers in that shop were another source of fascination to me. They were all nationalities and would gossip away, sharing their highs and lows of life with us behind the counter. The owner of the shop was called Marigold and her mother was Hetty.

Hetty lived a couple of doors away from the shop and was so strict with me, and if the conversation with the customers was not suitable, she would order me to the stock room. She would caution me as to what was suitable and what was not, and would always threaten to tell my father if she thought I was interested in something inappropriate.

I loved that lady, she was rich in life experience and, although stern, had a real quirky side to her character, and she would often have me laughing out loud.

Walking down Bute Street you would see three-storey Victorian houses, and these houses would represent all nationalities. You would find a Jamaican house with a cafe at the front, cooking and serving Jamaican food, as well as offering accommodation. There was a Chinese house, again with a café at the front, and so it would go on. These houses catered to the seamen but, of course, with the decline of the docks, their business had practically gone.

I believe that by this time I had stopped sensing that something else that seemed to be around me when I was younger. Religion was playing a lesser role in my life as well, and that was a real relief. Some times I would go to bed and forget to pray, and the next day nothing dreadful would happen, and so I got more and more relaxed about the whole thing. I was starting to think God wasn't as strict as I had been led to believe.

I was now fifteen and about to leave school with my Certificate of Merit. Our school didn't offer us CSE exams, as that was for the Grammar School pupils. I was not equipped to do anything other than a menial job, but my parents had saved to send both my sister and me to Cleves Secretarial College, where we were taught shorthand, typing and book-keeping. I took to the shorthand and typing with ease. That was a lovely period for me, and I will always be grateful to my parents for having the vision to equip the both of us for life. I know that it was a great financial sacrifice to them, and they both had to work hard to accomplish it.

At college I was mixing with girls whose background were different from mine. In fact there were very few people from a council estate. Quite a few of the girls were from wealthy backgrounds, and I found it all fascinating.

This was the time of a music revolution. Soul and tamala motown hit the British music scene. We used to go to the

Top Rank on a Saturday morning and dance to Diana Ross and the Supremes, Marvin Gaye, Otis Reading, Sonny and Cher, as well as groups such as The Beatles and Jerry and the Pacemakers. All colours and nationalities would pack in to that dance hall. There was no colour distinction among the young and, in fact, I think we white kids admired the black kids because a lot of the music our generation loved was from the black population.

My social circle began to widen and I was starting to take my first steps out in to the world as a young adult. I had little judgement of what was appropriate or inappropriate behaviour by others, and I was used to human tragedy, as it was all around me. I didn't have any opinions of my own, and was quick to feel sorry for people, and here I was being let loose.

My year at college was up, I had finished my Saturday job and I was now sixteen years of age. My mother took me for a job interview in Mount Stuart Square, opposite the Coal Exchange in the Docks. It was with a firm of maritime solicitors called Lean and Lean. Roydon Dickinson Lean was the senior partner, and it was he who interviewed me, or rather he asked the questions and my mother answered.

I sat looking around his office, which had files piled everywhere. They were all on the floor and on shelves around the walls. There were also enormous leather-bound books with paper book-markers hanging out of them. I wondered how on earth he would ever know where anything was. My mother did a superb job for me, and I was to start work within a few days.

I had fantastic training in that office. Everything had to be done just right, and learning all the new legal terminology was like an introduction to another language.

Every morning I would be given dictation either by Mr Lean senior or his son, Mr John Lean junior. I would type away on a black Adler manual typewriter with my tippex erasure sheets near to hand. Those were the days when you would have a letter head, carbon and white paper in the machine, so that you could make a copy for the file.

I was the office junior and was also responsible for answering the phone, making tea, going to the shops to get everyone's lunch, as well as doing the banking and post.

When I was out of the office I found everything so interesting. As well as being a commercial area, it was still a red-light district. Some of the things I saw were unbelievable.

At lunch time the prostitutes would always be strolling around the square. They would blend in with the office workers but I could identify most of them because of seeing them outside the Custom House pub. They would try to make eye contact with the men. There was a large black lady called Sadie, and she would blow kisses at me if I looked at her and I knew she recognised me from the delicatessen. To me she seemed really frightening and I would keep my eyes to the ground when I saw her coming, but I couldn't resist a peep and she would always catch me looking.

My mother would make my father take me to work and pick me up whenever his shifts allowed, as my parents were worried about me being there. More than once I was propositioned by kerb crawlers as I walked along. I was advised by my mother to walk on the inside of the pavement, to deter anyone from grabbing me and bundling me in to a car.

This was the year that my seventeen-year-old sister Gail married a man of mixed race. He was twenty-five and seemed so sophisticated. He was also very handsome.

Although our community was made up of differing races, it was still difficult for the older generation to accept mixed marriages. The younger generation had such a different attitude, as we were used to this integration.

My parents quite rightly felt Gail was far too young to make such a life-changing decision, and they agonised over the rights and wrongs of her choice. However, once Gail's daughter Tracy was born my parents were immediately besotted, and her new husband proved himself to be such a nice person, he worked really hard for my sister and the baby.

When Tracy was born she was beautiful. Her skin was a light coffee colour; she had large, deep brown eyes and lots of black hair. She didn't look like a new baby at all. My sister said all the nurses in the hospital fussed over Tracy, and kept taking her off to show to various people. I loved being an aunty and sometimes would take Tracy into town, supporting her on my hip, and pretending she was mine. The feeling of love I experienced for this child was very powerful. Over the years some of my cousins have also married different races, and when we all get together we are so proud of all our children, and we truly are a rainbow family.

As my sister was now living with her husband and baby, living at home there was just mum, dad and me.

After a year at Lean and Lean I decided I had learnt sufficient to apply for jobs of a higher status. I didn't want to stay as an office junior for too long. I looked around for another job, and was thrilled to be interviewed and accepted to work for a firm of solicitors on Newport Road.

This firm offered a whole range of legal services. I was to work in the matrimonial department as a shorthand typist. Eventually, and as a result of my shorthand skills, I was sometimes asked to do the preliminary interviews with clients.

I would take down their statements, and get them to fill in legal aid forms. The things that went on behind closed doors were mind-blowing. Some of our female clients were living in really abusive situations. They would suffer all types of cruelty at the hands of their partners, and yet they continuously attempted reconciliations. It was always the children who suffered in these situations. Sometimes a separated or divorced mother might take a new man into her home and he would resent her children. One woman told me that for about four years her eldest son was not allowed to sit at the dinner table with the rest of the family as the step-father wouldn't eat with him. He said the boy made him feel sick. The mother accepted this, justifying her actions by reasoning she had to 'keep the peace'.

We had such a mix of clients in that office. I remember a really small man in his late twenties called Tiny. His wife had thrown him out of the family home because he was an alcoholic and was also addicted to barbiturates. Tiny would turn up in reception without an appointment and he would be passed to whoever was free, and so all the staff knew him. He was a real character.

One day he came in and a few of us were stood around him talking. He was saying he wanted to give up the drink and drugs and go home to his wife and children. We were all praising him and encouraging him in his way of thinking. A colleague called Chris asked him if he had any drugs on him, and Tiny confirmed he did. To emphasise how serious he was, Tiny told Chris she could have all his drugs, and he handed some tablets over to her. Chris kept saying to Tiny 'Are you sure you want to do this?' and he would answer 'I really, really do want to go home. I've had enough.'

When Tiny left the office he said he was going home to his wife and children and we were all waving him off, telling him to be strong. We stood around Chris and she was asking

'What should I do with them?' I said 'Flush them down the toilet Chris.' And she did. That was that, and we all went back to work feeling really happy.

About three hours later Tiny was back. He looked really awful. He was sweating profusely, his eyes were wild and he was talking fast, while licking his lips constantly. He asked to see Chris, and a whisper went around the offices. We all knew what he was there for, and couldn't believe the situation we were in.

The partners of the firm knew nothing of what had taken place earlier, and the reception was full of clients. Poor Chris had to go out and face Tiny. I was made to go with her, because it was my idea to flush the tablets down the toilets. The others were stood huddled together, watching from a safe distance. Chris told Tiny what she had done and he went ballistic. He was screaming at her, and we backed away from him but he kept coming forward. The receptionist dialled the police emergency number, and one of the senior partners came rushing out of his office. The whole place was in chaos.

Chris and I had to lock ourselves in the ladies toilet, and Tiny was kicking the door. Within a short while the police came and they had a hard job restraining Tiny. Eventually he was taken away. All of us involved in the incident were given a severe reprimand for our stupidity.

A few weeks after this incident we heard that Tiny and a couple of his friends had been burned alive when a derelict building they were sleeping in caught on fire.

One of the senior partners specialised in crime. He would very often take me from the matrimonial department and send me on some task for him. He regularly sent me to the local Whitchurch Hospital, which specialised in mental health. I had to take statements from patients who had drug problems and had committed various petty crimes to feed their habit. Some of the patients had irreversible brain damage through drug abuse, and I had to get used to being 'touched up' on a regular basis.

There was one patient called Gerald who would always be around when I visited. He continually changed his clothes. One minute he was dressed for the day, then he would disappear and return dressed for bed. On and on it went, and this was how he spent his day. He would trot back and forth strumming an imaginary guitar between changes. I was told he had gone on the hippy trail in the East and had taken bad acid. He was on a constant trip.

The firm also dealt with murder cases, and some of the information I was privy to was dreadful. I witnessed all kinds of human perversion, cruelty and tragedy.

We dealt with one murder where an Asian couple had murdered their son's girlfriend and her young child. Their justification was that the son had dishonoured them. They wanted an arranged marriage for him, but he would have none of it. When they were brought to trial and found guilty, the son hanged himself.

Another time the body of a baby was found buried in a local park, and the mother was found and charged with infanticide.

There was also a pornography case, and I couldn't believe the sickening images I saw. They were of animals and children, and the guilty people were quite clearly shown in the photographs. They had made no attempt to hide themselves, thinking they were above the law and would never be caught.

In the lunch hour I would walk with some of my colleagues the short distance into the town centre. Very often when we left

25

the building a midget man would be waiting for us. He was always dressed really smart. The moment he saw our little group he would hurl obscenities at us. None of us knew him and had no idea why he singled us out, but he would follow us into town. He would shout 'Whores the lot of you, children of Satan, prostitutes that's what you are, nothing but dirty prostitutes'. We were mortified but would giggle to hide our embarrassment. We would manage to lose him and then more often than not we would bump into Thelma.

Thelma was a lady who at that time would have been in her forties. She was tall and slim, with frizzy, light brown hair. She wore longish, flowing, flowery dresses and had the mind of a child. She would dance around us and lift her clothes up, showing her underwear. Nearly the whole of Cardiff knew Thelma and she loved to be in town, weaving her way around the people. She would link arms with the men and spin them around.

We would sit in the gardens by the Museum with a sandwich and a drink, and Thelma would join us. She was so vulnerable, and we would tell her she wasn't to keep lifting her clothes up, and then off she would go, dancing in and out of the people.

About this time I had discovered drugs myself. They were everywhere. I experimented with speed and LSD. The speed made me hyper active and I would continually talk, had little appetite and sleep was very difficult. The LSD was powerful and gave a heightened sense of euphoria. I loved my work and once I realised the drugs were not compatible to working life, I only took them at restricted times.

I went to the Isle of Wight Pop Festival to see Jimi Hendrix, Melanie, The Doors, Jethro Tull, Supertramp, Leonard Cohen, Joan Baez and many others. I went regularly to live concerts, travelling all over the country to see such acts as

The Rolling Stones, Queen and The Who. There are not many people or groups I haven't seen perform. I have a deep love of music, and my favourite artist is the late singer Kirsty MacColl, but regrettably I never saw her perform live. I love the way she wrote and sang about life, and I think we can all relate to so many of her lyrics.

Two

Suffer it and grow

I had lived amongst human dysfunction and tragedy, but I was an observer. This was other people's lives and I was cushioned. I had developed dysfunctions of my own and these took me down a path where I had to suffer in order to feel the pain.

Although I was learning about life, and despite taking drugs, I was still an innocent and still had bad judgement.

I was now seventeen and this was when I met Billy. He was the singer in a local rock band. Billy was very thin and full of energy. He was the life and soul of the party, and he and I were instantly attracted. I hadn't really had a proper boyfriend up until this time, but we soon fell in love. He told me stories of his childhood that immediately aroused my compassion. He had been brought up on a farm in West Wales and was the third of four children. His mother had died when he was five and his father had struggled to keep the farm and home going, as well as raise the children. There were times when Billy and his siblings had to go to a local children's home for short periods, as his father found it difficult to cope.

I saw Billy as a person who needed to be loved and looked after, and I set about mothering him. Very quickly he asked me to marry him. I was thrilled and agreed. I went in my lunch hour to a local department store and bought my own engagement ring. Billy wasn't able to pay for it as he had no money, and he couldn't accompany me as he had things to do. The ring was white gold with artificial stones. I thought it was wonderful.

I soon realised that Billy's life was chaotic. For instance, he drove a car and I discovered he had no driving licence, tax or insurance, and he didn't seem able to hold down a job. He appeared to borrow money and never pay it back. He would go to the pub with no cigarettes or money, and then others would have to support his drinking and smoking. Although I was mortified at this, he was completely nonchalant.

I began having second thoughts about being with him, and when he talked of us getting married I was worried, and decided it was not for me. When I told him he was inconsolable, and threatened suicide. He said he couldn't live without me. He begged me to marry him and promised he would be different, and so reluctantly I agreed. I felt sorry for him, and didn't understand he was not my responsibility.

Although having these faults, Billy was multi-talented. He could repair any engine, spray any type of vehicle and was fantastic at DIY and gardening. He seemed able to turn his hand to anything and people really liked him, as he was quite charismatic.

My father lent him money to start his own gardening business, and he had loads of work, but half the time he would be missing. My father was a particularly responsible person with regards to money and obligation. He would recommend friends to use Billy's services, and would be disgusted when Billy would let the friends down as Billy was ducking and diving, usually in and out of the pub.

I was trapped. I had to go ahead with the marriage because Billy was now my responsibility. I had an inner voice that was struggling to be heard, and it was opposed to my decision, but I squashed it. I could not contemplate Billy taking his life; I could never live with those consequences, and I did have feelings of love for him. Billy was happy for us to live in rented accommodation, but I was having none of it. I wanted to buy our own house and so my parents loaned us the money for a deposit on a three bedroomed terrace house in Splott.

It was 1971 and I was eighteen and Billy was twenty-three. A few days before the wedding Billy and I went with my parents to the local social club. We played a game of bingo and I said a prayer to God to let me win, as we were desperate for money. I won a house by calling on number twelve, and we were getting married on the twelfth, and this felt really strange. What a coincidence. Inside my head I said 'thank you', in case this was divine intervention.

Before our marriage the gardening business was closed, and Billy went to work as assistant manager of a hardware store. I was still working at the solicitors', and when we settled down to married life I worked out a schedule of outgoings that included paying back my parents. It was incredibly hard juggling our finances and it seemed natural that I would take responsibility for this.

At this time a dreadful thing started to happen to me. I would wake from sleep and be paralysed. I wouldn't be able to open my eyes or mouth. A weight would be bearing down on my body, but I was powerless to act. Inside I would be screaming and then I would hear a measured thump, thump, and thump noise, as well as a whooshing noise. Eventually I would come out of this but it used to make me fearful of going to sleep and my imagination worked overtime. These attacks were sporadic; they could be weeks or months apart.

After four years of marriage I became pregnant, and our son Kristian was born in 1975. I had worked full-time up until two days before he was born. I couldn't believe that this beautiful and perfect Pisces baby belonged to us. It was a wonderful experience for me to be a mother. The love I felt for my child overwhelmed me, just as it had with Tracy.

Shortly after this Billy was facing redundancy. Encouraged by me, he spoke to the company he worked for and asked if he could become a tenant at one of their shops. We were thrilled when he was offered the tenancy of a shop on the outskirts of Cardiff. I was so proud of him, and couldn't believe how much he had changed. The tenancy was put in our joint names, as we had to take out a loan against our property, but Billy kept me firmly away from the business, even though I felt I could have been an asset doing book-keeping. He was now firmly in control.

It was such a large shop in a busy area, and as well as being a hardware store it also had a grocery and newsagents section. It was really hard work, and nothing was automated in those days. Everyone mostly paid by cash, and the sales would be rung in to the till. I stressed to Billy he would have to be completely organised from day one and offered to help with the administration, but he wouldn't hear of it.

I was aware that Billy employed youngsters, but was upset when he started paying them to open up for him early in the morning and organising the newspaper runs. This was because he would get home so late in the nights, very often drunk, and he was finding it difficult to get up in the mornings. I constantly worried whether Billy had tight systems in place. There were no mobile phones in those days, and it soon became apparent that Billy was doing the usual ducking and diving. I could never get hold of him. I would phone the shop and youngsters would answer. They would never know where he was.

Kris saw very little of his father, and sometimes Billy would promise to be home early to see Kris before he went to bed. I would tell Kris that his daddy would be home, and he would be so excited. Many is the time I have watched my son fall asleep on the settee, having tried to keep himself awake for this magical appearance that never happened.

It was around this time that other strange things started to happen once more. I again had the feelings from my childhood, that vague sense of there being something else around me, but that something was not tangible and therefore unexplainable. I started to see objects move, but would doubt what I saw.

For instance, a picture might move back and forth, or a glass would move across the table. Lights would sometimes go on and off as if in code. They seemed to react to my having certain thoughts; it could be that I was questioning what I had seen, and on and off they would go. If I were on my own in the room, the television would turn off and then come back on. If someone was in the room with me, it never happened. I also started to see colours on my eyelids when I closed my eyes.

Although unhappy I didn't contemplate leaving Billy, because being a single parent was not really socially acceptable at that time. Everything appeared so complicated, and I didn't want the stigma of being a single mother. I had such high hopes for Kris and wanted him to have every opportunity to achieve.

In 1977 Kris was nearing two, and we were able to move to an area in Cardiff where the schooling was excellent, as well as being nearer the shop. I reasoned I should be content with my lot, although this was completely at odds with my inner voice, that intuition which was still struggling to emerge.

I didn't feel secure as I had so many questions. For instance, were the young boys opening up at the proper time? How would Billy ever know? It seemed to me the only time he would know would be if a customer complained. Also, were all sales going in the till? On and on the questions would beat in my head, but if I voiced them to Billy, that would be an excuse for him to march out and go to the pub, as he said I was nagging.

I knew I had to get control of my life and so I found Kris a part-time place in a nursery, and got myself part-time work at a firm of solicitors. I was to establish a matrimonial department for them. This was a fantastic opportunity, and I was so happy about it. The solicitor I worked for was on the duty rota at Central Police Station.

One day he was called to represent a man who was to be charged with murdering a local woman. The man was charged and refused bail, and so was on remand in Cardiff Prison. He kept demanding his solicitor visit him, and I would be sent in the solicitor's place. This client had a thick northern accent, and he was in his twenties. He had come out of the army the year before and had wandered around the country.

He quite liked the idea of a young woman visiting him, and one day the prison sent word he wanted to confess to the crime he'd been charged with, but he would only confess to me. I went with my shorthand pad and pencil at the ready. I spent around an hour with him, and what he told me was sickening. Apparently he arrived in Cardiff by train and had no particular reason for visiting the City. He was wandering aimlessly from place to place. He said he was head-shot; feeling totally depressed and was unable to stay with his family.

He found his way to a pub near to the city centre. In the pub he met a young woman who was also homeless. They started asking around the pub if anyone would give them a bed for the night. One of the regulars at the pub was a lonely alcoholic lady. She was a tragic figure, and her life experiences had sent her on a spiral of self-destruction, and she was drinking to dull the pain.

This awful man described to me in detail how he killed this lady who had offered him and his new companion a bed, and sex was part of his motive. I knew he enjoyed telling me this, and I struggled to stay professional, scribbling furiously away on my shorthand pad. I rushed back to the office to type the statement, and passed it on to the solicitor. He asked me to go back to the prison with him to get the statement signed, but this time I refused. I didn't want to be near such evil.

One of the clients was a man in his forties called Alan. He was a long distance lorry driver. He lived with his wife and child in a house they had bought on mortgage. Alan was a real workaholic, and took his role as provider for the family seriously. He was in a state of shock when his wife told him she wanted a divorce. She alleged the hours he worked were unreasonable, and said she was left to bring up their child virtually single handed. Alan was so distressed about the situation. His wife refused to discuss it with him, and he poured out his anguish to me. He kept repeating he had done nothing wrong, except work long hours to bring in the money.

While the divorce proceedings were going along, Alan came to me in the office and told me he had discovered his wife was having an affair. He had been given an anonymous tip-off about his wife and her relationship with a good friend of the family. Alan sat crying. He felt so injured and couldn't comprehend his wife had lied and schemed.

Apparently, acting on this tip-off, Alan pretended he was working away but in fact had stayed in the area, and was watching his house. He had followed his wife when she left the house, and she went to the friend's home. Alan sat outside for about an hour. He saw his wife and friend leave the lounge and walk up the stairs to the front bedroom. The curtains in the bedroom were then closed and the light went off. Alan left the scene as he had seen enough. He now knew the truth.

He stayed with me in my office for about an hour, and I used every ounce of energy I had to get him stable. He was in such grief and shock, and I was worried. I made him coffee and eventually he pulled himself together. He hugged me and said he felt better, and told me I wasn't to worry as he would be fine.   Two days later he was found in the cab of his lorry.   He had gassed himself.   I felt bereft and kept going over our meeting, torturing myself.   I was one of the last people to have seen him alive.   This incident had a profound effect on me for quite a while.

Meanwhile, I started to go out and about on my own, getting a life again. Kris was safe, as he was with my parents at those times.   They were fabulous grandparents to him and Tracy, and loved having them.   One night I met a young man who was studying civil engineering in Cardiff University, and I began seeing him behind Billy's back and, although this relationship was short-lived, I felt very guilty. I had a fabulous time with my student and this made me all the more discontent at home.

At this time a tragedy happened. Billy's father died suddenly. A few days after his death Billy and I were in our house and we were arguing. A photograph of his father was on top of our television. It came off the television and went through the air to the other side of the room where we were stood, landing at our feet. Billy immediately said 'That's my father, he doesn't want us to argue', and we both sat like a pair of frightened kids.   In my mind I thought 'Now there's intelligence with these happenings'.

Kris was now about two and a half years old and one day my sister Gail asked if I would go out with her that evening. I didn't really want to go, but she persuaded me. I couldn't get hold of Billy to tell him, but thought I would be out and back before he got home. My parents had Tracy and Kris, and we went in to town.

Walking in St Mary Street, we were discussing where to go but couldn't make up our minds. Over the road was a pub called The Philharmonic.   It still stands there to this day. We had never been in there before, and decided to pay a visit. We bought our drinks, sat at a table, and my sister said to me, 'Yvonne, don't look now but there's Billy.' When I looked, there was my husband stood at the bar with his arms around a young girl, and she was very pregnant. I couldn't believe what I was seeing. It was so confusing to see him stood there. I had never heard him mention this pub before, and didn't even know he came to town to drink. I always assumed he drank at a pub near the shop, but could never ask him, as he always denied he did any such thing. I told my sister I wanted to leave without him seeing us. We did this and I went straight home.

I sat in the lounge in a darkened room waiting for Billy to appear. He came in at about one in the morning and jumped out of his skin when he saw me sitting there in the dark. He said 'What the hell are you doing?' and I said 'I have been to the Philharmonic and saw you'. Billy immediately dissolved, he sobbed and admitted guilt. He said it was an accident; he didn't love the girl and didn't want the baby, but didn't know what to do. I told him I was leaving and taking Kris with me, and he immediately said he would take his car, drive on the motorway and kill himself. I remember saying to him 'If you do that, please make a good job of it as I will not be sitting at your bedside, and make sure you don't take anyone else with you'.

In my head I thought back to when I'd tried to break off my engagement to him, and he had kept me with him by threatening the same thing. I had an inner knowing that I'd come a long way from that time. I also recognised I didn't love Billy, and had not loved him for a long time.

I was surprised that such a massive coincidence had occurred, and how this chain of events had revealed the truth about Billy. Sleeping in the bed on my own that night, I had my eyes closed and saw part of an eye on my eyelids. I tried to bring this eye in to focus, but it kept disappearing. Eventually I fell asleep.

Billy was distraught I'd found him out. He couldn't pull himself together, and would beg and plead for me to stay. I told him I wanted the house sold and my name taken off the shop. He came out fighting, and said he had nothing all his life, he had worked really hard and was not about to have me take it all away. One minute he was nasty, the next he was crying and pleading. I began to feel sorry for him, and also felt guilty that I had been seeing someone without him knowing.

These feelings led me to agree to sign over the house and business to him, in exchange for the sum of £3,000. I knew all about the divorce laws and what I was entitled to, but I agreed this sum out of compassion and guilt. I was in fact entitled to double that amount, but by accepting the lesser sum it meant that Billy could keep the house and business. It never occurred to me that Billy wasn't interested in how Kris and I would manage. It was all about him and how he would manage. I bought a run down and neglected two bedroomed terraced house in Roath, Cardiff, which cost me about £6,000. I had difficulty getting a mortgage, as in those days single mothers were not looked on as viable, but through my legal contacts I achieved this. Kris and I were out of the old house within twelve weeks of everything happening.

The reality of day-to-day living in my new circumstances began to sink in. I had agreed Billy could have reasonable access to Kris, and he agreed to pay maintenance to Kris and me at the rate of £7 per week each. With my legal work and the maintenance we would just about manage.

At this time I had a visit in work from a lady called Debbie. I was told she was in reception with a baby in her arms, but I didn't know who she was. When she was shown in to my office I recognised her as the pregnant girl Billy had been with. I was flabbergasted. I asked her what she wanted, and she said she didn't really know, but she and her baby were on their way to a hostel. She knew where I worked and felt compelled to come to me. I asked her why she wasn't going to live with Billy in his house, and she said he told her the house was now mine. Apparently her parents had told her to choose between them and Billy. She could go home to them with the baby if she would finish with him, but she was in love with him and so refused. I couldn't believe what I was hearing, and again all those feelings of compassion and nurture came to the fore, this time for Debbie and her baby.

I still had the keys to Billy's house, and I asked my boss if I could leave work early, to which he agreed. I took Debbie and the baby to a local shop to buy provisions, and then I drove them to Billy's house. I let them in, made them comfortable and phoned Billy. When he knew what I had done he was outraged, and said he would never forgive me.

My divorce from Billy took place in 1978. Over the next few months Billy would pick Kris up on a Sunday. He would sometimes take Tracy with them, and they would have a really good time. The only down side was that very often Billy wouldn't have the maintenance money. I would have to argue with him in front of the kids, and it used to spoil the occasion. I quickly realised I couldn't regard Billy's money as disposable income, and so looked for something to supplement my earnings.

A good friend of mine called June was working at party plan selling pottery, and so I joined her and became an agent working some evenings and weekends. It was a good thing I did because shortly afterwards Billy didn't turn up on his regular Sunday visit. There was no phone call from him, or any other attempt at communication. Kris had his little bag packed to go swimming, and he was devastated. He was three years of age and was making all sorts of excuses for his father. He said things like 'Perhaps daddy has forgotten our address,' and 'Perhaps daddy is ill'. Kris was never to see his father again. I found out through friends that Billy had taken off to Spain. He had split from Debbie, sold the house to a friend of his, and handed the tenancy of the shop back to the company.

We never received another penny in maintenance, even though eventually I was told Billy was back in the UK, and was living once again in West Wales. I would never have attempted to collect the money due from him, reasoning that if he couldn't give it with a good heart, then we didn't want it. Kris repeatedly asked had I heard from Billy, was there a letter from him or perhaps a telephone call? His behaviour became quite aggressive at times, and I knew that my poor son was hurting, and I was hurting for him.

During the next three years our lives were happy. I was working two jobs, and was fortunate enough to have my parents as unpaid baby sitters. Kris was a joy. He was such a loving child. He was a very practical and hands-on little person, and from two years of age he used to bath himself and wash his own hair. When my friends Mary and Tony's little boy Nathan came to stay, Kris would also bath Nathan and wash his hair and then go on to dry and dress both of them.

At that age Kris could even make a cup of tea. If you gave Kris a tool kit and an old alarm clock, he would be in his element. I used to give him wood and he would cut and hammer, experimenting with joins. He was six when he changed his first plug. My mother gave him the job to do for her, and I couldn't believe he'd done it.

In February 1981, on Kris's sixth birthday, a party was in full swing in the house, and there was a knock on the door. Kris answered, and there stood a taxi man with a box of toys. He told Kris they were from his father. The excitement was high as Kris and his friends unpacked the box, and I watched my son's reaction closely. He seemed fine and really pleased with the presents. When everybody went he sat on my lap, sucking his thumb and said 'If Billy sends presents again, will you take them to the children's home?' and I said 'Why Kris?' and he said 'Because he didn't bring them himself'. I couldn't grasp that a six-years-old child could think on such a deep level, and looking at my son I felt humbled. How had Billy and I ever produced a child such as this?

Later that evening Kris and I were tidying up. One of the presents Billy had sent was a fishing rod. A hook from the rod was on the floor, and as I picked it up the hook went through my thumb. There was a barb on the end, and there was no way I could get the hook out. Kris and I went to the local casualty department. As we were standing at the counter, a blonde lady came up to me and said 'Are you Yvonne?' and I told her I was. She said 'I am Debbie's mother. She is over there, and has just pointed you out to me. I want to ask you a question that's been on my mind for a long time. Did my daughter break up your marriage?' and I told her 'No', and I said she was not to worry about that. I went and spoke with Debbie and saw her child, but had a really strange feeling. That inner voice was there again, and I began to think of the possibility that this sequence of events was no coincidence.

During the next year Kris and I moved house twice, firstly to a larger house directly across the road from us, and then to a three bedroomed house very close to my parents. I was proud of what we were achieving on our own. Our homes had always been happy and there were always other people's kids there. Sometimes Kris would have up to four children sleeping over. I had a good circle of friends and they would always come to me in a crisis. I always seemed to know what they should do, and was very quick to help and, in fact, would

41

give over and above what was required of me. I am a very positive person and could infuse my friends with my positive way of looking at things.

I was also dating various people, but most of them I kept away from my son. I had let one boyfriend get close, but had quickly realised that again I had poor judgement, and broke off my relationship with him. That inner voice was at last getting through to me.

I had left my job at the solicitor's because my salary was quite low, and I was also feeling weary of the emotional nature of the job. I found an excellent position working as a PA to the Managing Director of a marketing company, as well as doing the party plan. Between the two jobs I was earning really good money, it was 1982 and Kris was seven.

It was winter time and the snow was thick. I was walking to work with great difficulty and a man driving a large four-by-four vehicle stopped and offered me a lift. I recognised him from around the area. I was grateful to accept and he introduced himself as Michel. Michel was a first generation Italian. He came to Cardiff when he was two-years of age, along with his elder brother Paolo and their mum and dad. He was a real ladies' man, and immediately made a play for me. He looked up my telephone number in the directory and began calling me on the telephone and I was terribly flattered, but after a couple of days of his attention, and as a result of his asking me out, I asked him if he was married. He replied, 'Yes I am, but what has that got to do with you coming for a drink with me?' I was so disappointed and also quite offended, and my tone relayed this to him. He then left me alone.

About six months later I bumped into him. He immediately asked me out again, and when I reminded him that he was a married man he said, 'Well that is where you're wrong. My wife has left me for another man and I could really do with someone to talk to'. He told me that he was in a bad way emotionally. My instinct was that he was distasteful to me, despite a physical attraction, but he said he was hurting and so I felt sorry for him. I met him and we had a nice couple of hours together, and I told him I thought his difficulties were karma, 'what goes around comes around'. He had been very willing to meet with me while married, and his wife had gone a step further. He wouldn't accept this, and said his actions with me were a symptom of their failing marriage, but he hadn't realised why the marriage was failing until it was too late. He talked a good story, but my inner voice was now working and I was having none of it.

When I left I wished him well, but made it clear I wouldn't be seeing him again. He called me over the next week, but I was quite non-communicative. One day I arrived home and there he was on my doorstep. I was really irritated by this, but his eyes filled with tears, and he said he just needed to talk. This set the pattern for the next few weeks. Sometimes I would be quite rude to him and tell him I was busy, but I felt so guilty when he walked away. He would look so miserable.

One time he asked me out, but I refused his offer and I told him I was meeting my friend June. She and I regularly went to a wine bar. We were in the bar having a drink and in walked Michel. He came straight over to me. I asked him what he was doing there and he said 'I only came to buy you both a drink, can't I even do that?' He bought us a drink, but I let him know he was intruding. He was so pushy, and I wasn't comfortable with it. When Michel called at the house Kris would sometimes be there, and he was lovely with Kris. This was something in his favour.

Two awful events happened at this time. We were given devastating news. My mother's youngest sister Maureen had cancer. She had been unwell for a while, and when she eventually had an exploratory operation, it was discovered she had bowel cancer. Her bowel was removed and she had a colostomy bag. She was only forty-eight. While Maureen was in hospital recovering from the operation, my grandmother Beatty died. She had heart failure. We were all inconsolable. My mother was distraught and poor Maureen had to be told. I remember rushing to my nana's house when I heard she had collapsed, and seeing her lying on the floor. My cousins and my mum were there, and it was awful. When my nan was taken to the funeral home, I went to do her makeup, as she always liked to look nice. I felt no fear, and had an inner knowing that I could talk to her and she would hear.

Maureen came home to a very different house than the one she had left. My nan had always been there, and it must have been so traumatic for her. She was desperately ill. My poor mother was falling to pieces and couldn't cope with the loss of her mum, and her sister's obvious decline. The months went by and Maureen was struggling to survive. I had a thought in my mind that wouldn't go away. Something kept telling me that Maureen would die on Kris's birthday.

In 1983 we celebrated Kris's eighth birthday at home, and my mother was with us when Emrys called to say Maureen had taken a turn for the worse. My mum and I rushed to the house. Maureen was clawing the air, fighting for breath. There was oxygen on hand, but now it had no effect. I sat in a chair and tried to reach her with my mind. I was saying 'Please Maureen stop fighting, let go, let go'. I was also speaking to my nan in my mind, asking her to come for Maureen. I didn't know if any of this would do any good, but it felt right to do it.

All the family were with Maureen when she took her last breath. She was such a fantastic and loving lady and her husband and four children were distraught. It was such a relief that she'd gone and would have no more suffering but I was stunned that it had happened on Kris's birthday, just as I'd thought. I went home crying and exhausted. In the night I was woken by my aunt's voice very softly calling my name, 'Von, Von'. I shouted 'Where are you?', but no answer came back. On my eye lids were beautiful colours of purple, and then changing to lime green, and then back to purple.

After my aunt's death I became ill. When I was fifteen my appendix had burst, and as a result of poison escaping into my system, I suffered with cysts on the ovaries. I had two previous operations to remove cysts, and I recognised the symptoms. It was so upsetting to be told by the specialist that I had to be admitted to hospital immediately. This would place a real burden on my parents. My sister would help out, but they would have Kris full-time. My mother was still very distressed over her mother and sister's death, and Michel came to the rescue. He insisted he could make life easier. He said he would liaise with my mother and help out. Telling Kris what was happing was less traumatic, as I was able to assure him Michel would bring him to see me constantly. Michel also gave Kris the incentive of visits to the park on the way home from the hospital. My mother was grateful for this help, and so now my attitude towards Michel changed. I had become indebted to him.

Michel was as good as his word, and displayed a real caring side to his nature. Kris was in and out of the hospital, always happy and laughing, telling me where Michel had taken him. When my parents would visit, they would express their gratitude that Michel was such a help.

When I came home from hospital Michel presented me with tickets for a one-week holiday for the two of us in France. It was all paid for, and my parents had already agreed they would take care of Kris. I felt uneasy about that, but it was done. I could not turn him down, after all it was a generous gesture, and he had paid for the holiday in advance. I had only ever been to Jersey, and so visiting France was lovely, but I wouldn't have chosen to go. My wonderful son had been away from me too long, and I would have preferred to be with him, or taken him with us. Also my parents deserved a break, and so I carried quite a bit of guilt to France.

Michel and I came back from the holiday a proper couple. That inner voice was still shouting but I reluctantly ignored it. I had been treated like a princess by Michel, but he had also made me feel responsible for him. He had the opportunity to pour out all his unhappiness, and he took full advantage. He told me he loved me, and wanted to be with me. He wanted us to live together and I agreed. There was no going back, I was in too deep. I had started to feel sorry for him, and the mothering instinct was rearing its ugly head.

After our holiday, I went for a night out with my sister. We met up with a few other people, and one of them was Michel's boss's wife. The wife asked me who was looking after Kris, and I said Michel. She asked why he was looking after Kris, and I told her we had been seeing one and other for a while. She abruptly stood up, said something to her friend, and both of them left. I was astonished. What had I done? Her departure was so rude. My sister and I couldn't understand. I went home and told Michel and he didn't make much of a comment.

The next day I got a call from his boss. Apparently Michel and the boss's wife had been having an affair, and his wife didn't know about my relationship with Michel. The boss said his wife blurted this out to him on her return home from the previous night. She told him Michel had stopped seeing her a few months before, and she couldn't understand why but, after meeting me, she had her answer. Michel's boss was devastated and out for Michel's blood, and I was equally devastated. The boss and his wife split up shortly after that.

I told Michel I never wanted to speak to him again. He cried, begged and pleaded, but I would have none of it. Unbeknown to me he begged my sister to meet him. She did, and he really sold himself to her. He told her when his wife left him he had been in a terrible state, and the boss's wife had consoled him, and in a moment of weakness he had given in to temptation. He said as soon as he started going out with me he had stopped seeing her, but she was like a stalker and he was frightened of her, and so hadn't told her about seeing me.

I was in a terrible state because of what had happened. I let myself be persuaded that Michel had acted out of character, even though my inner voice was trying to caution me. It seemed such a huge thing to keep him out of our lives, when all of us had already bonded. I can make no excuses for my weakness, and looking back I shudder with distaste at the person I was then. Michel kept working in the same place and had no problem seeing his boss, the man he had betrayed, every day.

Michel was living alone in the home he had once shared with his wife. She was pressing him for her share of the property, and so he decided to sell it. We were going to pool our money together and buy a larger house for the three of us. He got a buyer for the house very quickly, and he and his wife decided who would have what furniture. He was to replace some of my furniture with his furniture, and that way both of us would feel at home whilst temporarily living in my home. The sale went through, and we had a busy time sorting through his belongings. When he was firmly moved in, he dropped a bombshell. He had no money! Apparently his outgoings had been more than his income and he was heavily in debt. He had to pay off a load of debt, leaving him with no money. I couldn't believe it.

Kris was so excited that Michel had moved in, and I felt I couldn't ask Michel to leave, and once again circumstances in my life seemed very complicated, and my character was so weak. I couldn't bear to take the hard road and finish our relationship as I should have done. I still wanted to move house and Michel wanted us to buy a place together. If this was to happen I insisted Michel had to agree to have the value of the new house apportioned, to take in to account the money that I would be investing. He didn't want to do this, and we rowed bitterly. That inner voice was struggling to be heard again, and I was half listening. I reasoned if I protected Kris and me financially, then it would be all right to stay with Michel. He was so attentive and loving and Kris was really happy, and I was so very weak.

Meanwhile unbeknown to me Michel had been applying for jobs in different parts of the country. Working alongside his boss was becoming increasingly difficult as, although Michel had no problem with the situation, the boss understandably wanted him out. Michel was a Facilities Manager and was good at his job. It didn't take him long to get an offer from a company in Bristol. Once he had the offer he sat me down and told me of the opportunity. He wanted us to move near to Bristol and had details of property for sale in the Chepstow area, which is near to the Severn Bridge that links Wales and England. Chepstow is on the Welsh side and Bristol is on the English side of the bridge. Chepstow is approximately thirty miles from Cardiff. It would mean I would have to leave my jobs, as the hours would not fit around our family life, but the idea was compelling as it would be a fresh start for all of us.

We moved within the year, and I had my way with the apportionment of the property. I owned sixty percent, and Michel owned forty percent. This apportionment would carry over to every house we lived in. If the relationship fell apart Kris and I wouldn't lose out financially. Michel was really unhappy about this.

Our new home in Chepstow was lovely and the facilities in the area were wonderful. Kris loved his new school and was thriving. I found work as a sales executive, selling and merchandising designer sunglasses for a London based fashion house. Our family and friends in Cardiff were only half an hour car journey away and so we saw everyone weekly. We lived in that house for five years, and mostly they were happy times. We had acquired a rescue dog, a black Labrador called Lucky, and we all adored her. A couple of years before we had also acquired a cat we called Blue, and Lucky and Blue kept us all laughing, as they constantly vied with each other for attention.

Eventually we decided to move, and began to look for what we thought of as our dream home. We had been searching and searching for the right house, and eventually saw a likely prospect. It was a beautiful detached house, in a lovely setting, and in the same area as we were already living, but it needed so much work. Michel fell in love with it, but I told him it was too much for us to take on. He argued and cajoled. He said he could do all the work himself. I reminded him he detested DIY, and said I thought it would cause problems between us, but he persuaded me, against my better judgement. He said, 'I promise you I will do all the work myself, and I will not complain'. So that was it, the legal wheels were put in motion for us to buy the house.

Before the move I had a birthday, and Michel was to take me out for a special meal. I was so excited and when I got home from work, set about getting myself ready. When Michel came in he had a face like thunder. 'What's wrong?' I asked, 'Nothings wrong, why should there be?' he said, 'Because you have a face like thunder' I replied. 'If you are going to start, I am out of here' he said, and that was it. He walked out and took off in his car. I waited and waited, but he didn't come home that night. It was unbelievable; once again I was in a state of confusion, with the inner voice struggling for dominance.

The next day he came home with a present and a card for me. He said he was sorry about the night before, but the stress of the move was getting to him. I was so hurt, but didn't have the strength to argue with him. I felt so uneasy with that inner voice tugging at me constantly.

We moved to the new house in September 1989, and it was in a worse state than we first thought. The place was filthy. We had to take all the carpets up, and the curtains came down, because of the smell in the house. We set about cleaning, stripping walls, preparing paintwork and we employed an electrician and a plasterer. We were both continuing to work full time, and so we were tired. Kris and I would have music on whilst working away in the evenings and on weekends, but Michel was in a foul mood. He would complain we were making a noise, and say that he didn't want us doing any of the painting as we would make a mess. He was making life quite unpleasant.

After a month Michel asked if I would mind if he played tennis on the Saturday, he said he thought he deserved a break. I agreed and said for him to enjoy himself. He left Saturday morning at about eight, and said he would be back after lunch, around two. He arrived home about ten at night and said 'Sorry I'm late' and I said 'Sorry isn't good enough'. He said 'Oh f--- off then' and I said 'No, you f--- off', and he did. He went upstairs, emptied all his belongings into black bags, loaded up his car without a word to me, and drove off. I was stood in a house that had no carpets or curtains, the electrics weren't finished, and it was cold. I was in shock and sobbed and sobbed. Luckily Kris was with my parents.

Over the next few days I didn't tell anyone that Michel had left. I kept thinking he would come back. I hadn't heard from him, and didn't want to start ringing around looking for him. It was so humiliating. Kris kept asking for him, and I would say he had gone away with work. I had to put on a brave face.

After about two weeks I was starting to admit defeat and began to worry about the mortgage payments. Would he pay his share, and how would I manage? I called in an estate agent, with the idea of putting the house on the market, but was shocked to hear it had gone down in value because of its unfinished state, even though a lot of work had already been done. This presented a big problem for me. I was working out our finances, and realised if the house was sold I couldn't afford to stay in the area. Kris was now in high school and I wanted him to stay where he was. If I wasn't careful I would have a repeat performance of what happened when Billy and I had split up, and Kris and I would find ourselves back where we had started.

By now, Kris was aware something was wrong, and so I had to tell him Michel had left. I couldn't believe his reaction. He cried and cried, and made himself ill. I had to have the doctor to the house, as his throat was so swollen. He had tonsillitis and just laid on the settee in an unfinished room, wrapped in blankets in utter misery. I had to swallow my pride and ring Michel at work. He answered the phone and when he knew it was me, his manner was completely hostile. I told him we needed to talk, and he said he would call around that evening. I then had to tell my parents what had happened, and they came and took Kris home with them.

Michel called to the house, and he was so aggressive. He told me he was sick of me and said nothing he ever did was good enough. There were lots and lots of allegations made by him, and I couldn't relate to what he was saying. We seemed to be living in two different worlds. Who was this person he was talking about? I asked him if he was coming back, and he said 'no'. I found myself begging him, and telling him I would do anything he wanted to make things better. He said he would think about it. I asked him where he was staying, and he said the name of a friend of his from the tennis club. Michel didn't realise, but I knew this person through the legal world, and he was a solicitor.

We agreed that Michel would call me the next day with his decision. Two days passed and I didn't hear from him. Plucking up courage I rang his friend's number and asked to speak to Michel. 'Sorry but he's out at the moment' his friend said, and I asked him to tell Michel I had called. A few hours later Michel turned up at the house with his belongings.

From the moment Michel moved back, my inner voice was active and gave me no peace. Once again, when I was in bed and my eyes were closed, I saw an eye on my eyelids. This time it was clearer and the eye was half open. Christmas was approaching and I sat Michel down and said to him 'I know you're having an affair'. He looked shocked. 'Don't be so ridiculous' was his reply. I was so calm and certain, but I couldn't tell you how or why. I said to him 'If you have any feelings for me, you will tell me the truth', but he continued to deny my allegations. I told him 'I will catch you out', and he replied that I was 'losing it'.

Christmas Eve we were meeting up with my family for a meal in a local pub. When it was Michel's turn to buy drinks, although there was a bar in the room where we were sat, he went to the downstairs bar. This was where the telephone was. I saw my father get up and walk down the stairs. He came back up, and I heard him tell my mother Michel was on the phone. A little later Michel returned with the drinks and I just watched him.

I had long term friends who were Shirley and her husband Tony, and Kim and her husband Chris. I had worked with Shirley years before and Kim was Shirley's daughter. Tony and Shirley lived in Tintern, which is an area very close to Chepstow. Christmas morning the four of them came around to our house for a drink. When the first drinks were poured Michel said he was going out to buy more mixers. I told him there was plenty and he needn't worry. A little later Michel said he felt like smoking a cigar, and was off to the shop to buy some. Tony said 'It's Christmas day Michel. I think you should stay with your family'. Michel told Tony to mind his own business, and reached across to pick up his car keys. Tony clasped Michel's wrist and said 'Put the keys down'. I was stunned; it was as though there was an unspoken communication between all of us. I had honestly not voiced my feelings or suspicions to anyone. Michel backed off, and by the time our four guests were leaving, other guests were arriving for lunch, and it was as though the crisis was over. Michel became the perfect host.

The next day was Boxing Day and we spent this with Michel's family in Cardiff. When we left them we went for a walk with the dog. I said to Michel, 'I think you should come clean and tell me what's going on'. He refused. I told him, 'I promise you I will find out the truth, but it will be much better coming from you'. He did not deny there was anything going on but unkindly said 'Prove it'. I kept up the pretext of happy families until the celebrations were over but once they were over I knew what I had to do. My inner voice was telling me to look in Michel's car. Kris was to sleep at my parents the night after Boxing Day, and Michel was taking him. I hid Michel's car keys so he had to take my car.

Immediately he was gone I went to his car. In the boot I found a card with the name Pam on the envelope. On the front of the card was a latticed window with the profiles of two lovers outlined in the window. The inscription said 'To Pam with much love M'. There was a present wrapped in Christmas paper. I opened it and found a little box with a powder puff on the top, and a bottle of cheap perfume inside.

Despite feeling sick inside, I had to laugh at his choice of present. Pam was obviously no high-maintenance lady.

Michel came back to find me sitting on the sofa with the card and present to Pam next to me. 'I am allowed to have friends', was his cold reaction. I told him 'Get your things and get out'. He said he wouldn't go, and I told him he had no choice. I rang Shirley and she came straight around and sat with me while Michel collected his things. He left the house with a real attitude, and showed not one ounce of remorse. I took his betrayal very badly and his behaviour fuelled feelings of inferiority in me.

The next day I called my parents and told them what had happened. I had to tell Kris what had happened as he sensed something was wrong. I reassured him that we would be fine and asked him not to worry. My father brought him home later and told me Kris had been crying in the car. My father asked Kris what was wrong, and my wonderful eleven-year-old son told him 'I'm all right bamp, I'm not crying for me I'm crying for my mother'.

Over the next few weeks I set about taking control of my life. I rang Michel's tennis friend and told him I knew he had given Michel an alibi, and I wanted him to know that I knew. I told him I believed in karma and wished for him what he deserved, and I would leave it up to the universe to decide what that was.

I again had the house valued and this time, although I would still be losing money, I decided I had no other option. The estate agent couldn't put the house on the market without Michel's agreeing. Pam lived in Cardiff and I roughly knew the area she lived in and so Shirley and I drove there to see if we could see his car. As we turned on to the estate, there was Michel coming towards us. What a coincidence, it was incredible, the hairs on my arms stood up. I felt I had been led to him. The estate was like a rabbit warren, with quite a few different means of entry and exit. What were the chances of that happening, and the timing, it was stunning. Michel saw us and stopped his car. I got Shirley to go and speak to him. She was gone for ages, and when she came back she told me Michel was in a terrible state. He couldn't stop crying and was begging her to speak to me. He wanted to come back. That was a complete turn around. I couldn't take it in.

Shirley and I drove to a shopping area for coffee, and we were sat in the window of the café and Michel walked past. He locked eyes with me and gave me an imploring look. I looked away. He stayed staring at me, and tears started running down his face. I was sickened and told Shirley that he hadn't shed a tear when Kris and I were hurt, but now he hurt he was crying, and he was crying for himself.

Michel refused to put the house on the market, and the message he gave me was 'We can work things out'. Even though he was staying with Pam he would phone and beg me to take him back. He then started to appear at the door, and would ask if he could do anything for me. Sometimes I would call the dog and say she needed walking, other times I might tell him the rubbish needed to go out. He would do any chores I asked.

Two months went by and I became ill, the old symptoms of ovarian cysts appeared. I couldn't believe my luck. How would I manage with Kris, the animals, hospital and money? I told Michel if he really wanted to try again he had to tell Pam in front of me that he wanted to be with me. In the end he telephoned her from our house, and I listened on the extension. Kris didn't want him back, and said he couldn't forgive him for hurting me. I persuaded him that for now it was the best course of action.

Michel moved back in to the house, and two days later Pam rang me. She wanted to talk, and I knew now was my opportunity to find out the truth. It emerged that Pam and Michel had a relationship all through his marriage. She said when Michel's marriage broke down she was elated, and thought Michel would be with her. She then stopped hearing from him. Apparently Michel and Pam met up again three years after he and I had moved in to the first home we had bought together. She confirmed the night of my birthday, when Michel had stormed out, he was with her. They had stayed at a hotel together and she said this was because she didn't want Michel taking me out. So there it was, I wanted to know the truth and I had it. I could make no more excuses for any decision I made in the future. I now knew what he was. I felt absolutely worthless.

The day Pam rang I had an appointment at the hospital. I was told by the consultant that I needed a complete hysterectomy, and I was booked to have the procedure in two weeks' time. My life had turned into a hell. I would lie awake going over everything in my mind, constantly thinking what to do for the best. I believed that my present poor health was as a result of the stress I was under, and I vowed to never go there again. I knew it was my own fault, I had been given plenty of warning as to Michel's real character, and I hadn't listened.

Michel was being the model partner and father, but Kris and I were cautious. My first priority was to my son, but he was coping really well. He and I had turned a corner, and our emotions were no longer raw. It was like as though a spell had been lifted, and we had the upper hand in the situation. I became absolutely calculating. I did myself a check list of for and against staying with Michel, and I sat with Kim and went over the list. I valued her input more than anyone else's. We both agreed my main concern was Kris and his schooling, and to achieve my aims I needed Michel's income. There was a side to Michel that was fantastic, and when that side was dominant he made life so easy.

I sat with Michel and recounted to him everything Pam had told me. He cried the whole time. I told Michel I would work with him to rebuild our relationship, but the rules had changed. I said I needed constant reassurance from him, as I no longer trusted him, and if I wanted proof of anything he told me, then proof I had to have. He would have agreed to anything he was so desperate to stay.

A couple of days after the talk with Michel, my childhood friend Mary told me that Pam worked part-time in her sisters pub, and her sister told Mary that Michel was often in the pub and was regarded as Pam's partner. Then my old friend June told me her daughter worked in the same office as Pam, and Michel was regularly outside the office waiting to give Pam a lift. This all seemed unbelievable and I started shouting and laying down the law, but still I didn't walk away.

Time went by, I had my hysterectomy and Michel was a brilliant nurse. When I was back to full health I went back to work and our lives continued. Kris sat his GCSE school exams and achieved good passes in all the subjects he sat. This meant we could now move out of the area, as we were no longer tied to schooling. Kris could continue his education in a college in Cardiff. We had both decided we wanted to return to our roots and leave all the bad memories behind. Kris and I would discuss this when we were alone, and Michel was not a consideration.

One day I was visiting with Kim and Chris at their lovely home in Cyncoed in Cardiff. We took the dogs for a walk and on the walk we saw a beautiful house that was for sale. It obviously needed to have work done to it, but it was opposite open fields and woods and it really was perfect for us. I loved it and immediately took Kris to see it. He loved the house as well. I told Michel that Kris and I wanted to move from Chepstow and had seen a house we wanted to buy in Cardiff. Michel said it sounded a great idea, and then I dropped the bombshell that we had not discussed Michel coming with us.

Michel was devastated at this and cried bitterly. He pleaded with Kris and me to include him in our plans, and was very forceful in persuading us he had changed. After lengthy discussions between the three of us we agreed we would stay together as a family. Kris gave me the deciding vote, saying he would go along with what ever I wanted, as Michel no longer had an effect on him.

We put our house up for sale and began negotiations to buy the new house. We immediately got a buyer for our house. It was in my mind that I could still back out of our agreement with Michel and get away from him. I recognised I was quite cowardly and would always give in to Michel's distress but I half thought if I made the decision at the last moment, then there would be little time for emotions. Perhaps that way I could make the break. I am sure Michel sensed my thoughts, as he was just wonderful during this time. He would become very emotional about the past, crying and saying that he nearly lost me and Kris, and he would never forgive himself for his behaviour.

Once again the dreaded nurturing feeling overcame me, and I felt sorry for him. I was starting to recognise my pattern of behaviour. I could only come out fighting in response to a hurt, but once the hurt was over there would be no fight in me. My character had a huge flaw in it and I recognised this and was sickened by it, but instead of leaving him I prayed. I didn't know who or what I was praying to, as I had long ago relinquished religion, but I gave a plea to the universe. 'If there is anyone there, please help me. If Michel ever betrays me again, please let me be in a position, both emotionally and financially, to stand on my own two feet, so that I can leave him behind'.

We moved from our old house into a rented flat in Cardiff. This was a temporary arrangement as we were paying a builder to do the necessary work to the new house. I was not going the DIY route again. Walls had to come down, arches were created, and outhouses turned into a utility room. A new kitchen and bathroom was installed, as well as fitted wardrobes in all bedrooms. Everywhere was decorated. Fitted carpets and made to measure curtains completed the transformation. It was a dream home. I was so proud. Kris loved it, for him it was paradise. There was so much room and the views were fantastic, as the house was elevated.

Shortly after moving in to our new home, my childhood friend Beverly and her husband Howard visited. They mentioned they were buying a parcel-delivery franchise, but needed a partner to match their investment, and be responsible for marketing the business. I felt this was a timely opportunity for me. I had money I could call on, and there had been a thread of marketing all through my working career. Michel was not happy for me to do this but I saw the possibility of achieving financial freedom for Kris and I, should we ever need it.

This might be part of the answer to my prayer regarding Michel and his future behaviour. The first indication there was a problem between my friend and her husband came when we had just opened the business and she said to me, 'If a woman called Mandy rings asking for Howard, please will you tell me about it?'. 'Why?' I asked. 'Well she has been stalking him,' was the reply. Oh dear, there goes that inner voice.

The transport industry is really no place for a woman, except in the office. The front end of the business involves long hours and manual labour. The workforce is predominantly

59

male, and you need their respect and co-operation to make things work. This was Howard's domain. I was quite happy in the back office, which was my domain. Beverly would be in and out of the office, constantly checking up on Howard over the radio system when he would be out delivering goods. From the beginning, during his time out of the office, Howard would be ducking and diving. I found myself in the middle of a domestic dispute, and I was involved because his disappearing would have an impact on the business. If he was working a particular area and you couldn't give him instructions for delivery and collections, then it created a problem and service levels would drop.

Beverly eventually confided that the area Howard had allocated for himself to work was the area Mandy lived. When Howard's mobile bill came, there were pages upon pages of a number not known to me, but identified by Beverly as Mandy's. So there it was, Beverly had her proof that Howard was probably playing away, but where did that leave me? Beverly said she would sort it, but all that happened was increased ducking and diving by Howard, and more surveillance by Beverly.

I was in the office one day and a man entered and introduced himself as Eddie, Mandy's husband. He showed me documentation from Companies House stating Mandy and Howard had recently formed a limited company, and were operating a parcel-delivery franchise. Eddie said he was alerted when he discovered his wife had forged his signature to re-mortgage their home. She had used this money to buy the franchise that she and Howard were operating.

The penny then dropped, everything was sliding in to place. I thought of the form Howard had devised for me to fill in when I went on a sales call. The form required in-depth detail, listing all the visited company's details, their parcel movement, who was servicing them, the rates they were paying and the rate I was quoting. Howard was passing this information to Mandy, I was doing all the leg work and Mandy could then walk in and compete against my quote. He was also delivering and collecting goods on behalf of his other company, but utilising our vehicles and other resources. Our business was subsidising his other business overheads. I had difficulty understanding the logic of this but it was a fact, and it defied logic.

What a fool I was. Over and over again people played me, and I was sick to my stomach. Mandy's husband left and I telephoned Beverly. She came to the office, and I told her what had happened. She didn't show much of a reaction to my news. I explained I couldn't work with her husband, as you needed trust for a partnership. I asked her to get Howard to give me my money back and I could leave them to it. 'Leave it to me', she said. The next day I went to work, Howard was there and told me none of what I'd been told was true. I told him I'd seen the proof. He said Mandy's husband had forged documentation. I said 'So if I go to Companies House and do a search, I won't find what he showed me?' He said 'Well all I have done is offer a friend help, but the business is nothing to do with me'. I was getting nowhere.

I was desperately trying to listen to my inner voice and felt compelled, when I had the opportunity, to call the franchise head office, even though I knew once I had done this there was no going back. As franchisees Howard and I were bound by rules and regulations. I spoke to the Operations Director, and was stunned to be told they knew what Howard was doing and, in fact, were looking for a replacement franchisee. They were on the verge of taking the business away from us. They had received complaints about the service levels in our area and also had an anonymous tip-off about Howard being a director of the other business, which was in violation of our Franchise Agreement.

The Operations Director visited me that evening. He told me I could take over the franchise. If I didn't want that, then I would lose the money I had invested. I agreed to go it alone, and felt really strong in my decision. Howard and Beverly were bitter about losing their money, and neither wanted to take responsibility for what had happened. Howard refused to admit his guilt, and Beverly was aiding and abetting him. I hardened my heart to them and got on with running the business.

As I have explained, this was no business for a woman, and I struggled to familiarise myself with the running of the front end of the operation. I would be in work for quarter to six every morning, and not leave until about eight in the evening. Some of the men in my employ were Howard supporters, and did their utmost to sabotage my efforts. I had to let them go, and re-employ almost a new workforce.

I was becoming really hard when I needed to be. It was 1991 and Kris was sixteen and could look after himself; he proved a real asset at home. Michel was very supportive, and eventually started to open the business for me, and would then go on to his own job in Bristol. This enabled me to arrive at eight-thirty. Whilst there Michel would supervise the unloading of the parcels to be delivered, make up runs for the drivers and issue instructions for their day. I would organise and run the office, be out and about selling, do the accounts and have overall responsibility for the whole operation.

The more the business grew, the greater the problems became. There would be more money in, but increased overheads going out and, of course, at this time the country was in recession. Customers were demanding we cut their rates more and more, as other companies competing for their business were offering the same service for less money.

Running the business exposed parts of my nature I didn't know was there, and they weren't always attractive. Cash flow was a problem, and I was constantly telling half truths to the suppliers. I had to wear a mask and act positive in front of the staff and customers, always giving an image of control. If anyone in the business stepped out of line I could be deadly, and customers who didn't pay their bills on time had to run for cover.

I was dealt a crippling blow when the franchisor of our operation sold the franchise to a haulage company for £1. The haulier used our delivery network to prop up his ailing business, and within three months he went bankrupt. All the franchisees were owed large sums of money, and I was owed £35,000. The business world was no place for the faint hearted or anyone with a conscience, but still I plotted to survive yet another obstacle. My perseverance paid off as I became an independent, as opposed to a franchisee, having found a network that needed a South Wales partner.

At this time I started to wake at about three every morning. With my eyes closed I would see on my eyelids a square like a television, and in the square would be different, vivid scenes that had a three-d effect. One night there was a kitchen with a lady busying herself. She turned to me and waved. This really shocked me, as I had been quite content being an observer of these scenes, but the lady conveyed to me that she could see me as I could see her. Another time there was a farmer with cows around him, he also turned, and he doffed his cap at me. The square got bigger and bigger as the nights went on and eventually after a few months it was like a cinema screen, and always with different scenes being enacted.

One night the screen didn't appear. Instead on my eyelids, letters were tumbling. They came from the left, right, bottom and top. If I turned my eyes to the left or right for a closer look, they would disappear. I could only retain them by looking straight ahead, and they would be in my peripheral vision. Another night numbers came, and then another time faces. These faces were particularly fascinating and were both male and female, different ages and nationalities. Some would be face on, others sideways. They might be smiling or straight faced. I didn't know what to think but I was enjoying the show. I was getting better and better at seeing what was to my left and right, top and bottom, whilst continuing to look straight ahead.

Finally, one night on my eyelids, up in the far right hand corner, was a square. The square was really small but I knew there was something in it, as I could see movement. I strained to see what was in the square. Turning my eyes to the right was useless, as the square would disappear. I could only retain the square by staring straight ahead and it would stay in my peripheral vision.

The next night, and some nights after that, the same square would appear, always up in the far top, right-hand corner. Eventually I could see a little face inside the square. It was a little fat face all scrunched up, with the mouth puckered, and the eyes going back and forth. It was fascinating and I strained to see it. I could only retain it for a while and then it would be gone. Eventually I was no longer woken up at three in the morning. I would say the whole process had taken about four months. Afterwards, I would get visualisation on the eyelids at random times, and the colours would come often, as did the eye, which seemed to be opening wider.

Even though Michel was supportive of me, I still had this inner voice worrying me. There was something not right. I was so busy I didn't have time to monitor where Michel was, but reasoned he could not be up to his old tricks as he was as busy as me.

One day I was rushing through the warehouse and I fell over. I hit the concrete floor face first and was knocked unconscious for a few seconds. I went to the hospital for emergency treatment, as my head was cut and my nose had a piece missing out of the bridge. You could see through a hole in my nose to the inside. I was x-rayed but didn't have any fractures, but my nose was a problem. It couldn't be stitched as there wasn't enough flesh to bring it together. My face was swelling, and my eyes were blackening. Dressing was put over my nose, and I was given an appointment to return once the swelling had gone down. I was told I would need plastic surgery.

I went home and was in a terrible state. I hurt all over, and my emotions bubbled up and I couldn't stop crying. I was in torment. I had this intrusive inner voice that wouldn't give me any peace. I was frightened of life, and frightened to listen to this voice; I felt real self-loathing and couldn't bear any more pain. To calm myself I ran a bath. I lay back in the bath and in front of me was a near-empty jar of coco butter on the window sill. The jar had a plunger, and as I looked the plunger went down and the coco butter trickled out. I was so amazed I stood to have a better look, and as I did so I sensed my dead grandmother, Beatrice, with me. I could even smell her, and she wrapped her arms around me. The dreadful emotional and physical hurt rose from my body, and went out through the top of my head. I lay back in the hot water and felt a loving, comforting sensation that wasn't of this world. It was an exquisite feeling.

When the water cooled I came out of the bath, dried myself, scooped up the coco butter and, on automatic pilot, spread it over my head and face, including my nose. I got in to bed and slept the sleep of the dead. In the morning, although still bruised and swollen, the hole in my nose had closed. I couldn't comprehend what had happened. It was so spectacular I couldn't take it in.

This was such a stressful time and, even though I had now had a hysterectomy, I still had health problems. Over the years I had five abdominal operations, and I was now suffering with lesions. I needed to go in to hospital but it was impossible with our present situation. Again the universe provided a solution. The company Michel worked for closed. He did try to secure another position but it proved difficult. I did some re-organising of the staff and he came on to the payroll of my business and I went in to hospital. I was in hospital for ten days and Michel was amazing. He would come from work straight to the hospital to see me in the evenings, even though I would tell him not to. He assured me everything was fine in work and at home, and he seemed so laid back and happy.

I started to feel closeness with him missing for a long time. I was regaining trust. Since finding out the truth about him, he and I had lived together virtually like brother and sister. There would be the occasional physical contact, usually after a drink, but now I began to think we could put the spark back in our relationship. I felt love for him as he was being so kind. While in the hospital I told him how I felt, and said I wanted to put the business in our joint names in recognition of this trust. He was very emotional about this. I was wearing rose tinted glasses and saw a future where we were strong and together. I could see success in everything we did and I was so happy.

I left hospital on a Sunday with steel staples running from hip to hip. I was told to take things easy and not to drive. I woke around five on the Monday morning. Michel was lying next to me, and I felt overwhelming love for him. I wanted to wake him and tell him how I felt, to say I thought we were blessed to have our family, home, and a business we could share together. I also wanted to say I would come in to work with him, to be near him.

I had a thought come in to my head saying 'No, don't do that'. In my dreamy state I was completely taken aback, and thought I could sense my nana Beatty. I lay listening, but heard nothing. Was that thought voice real? On my eyelids were the vivid colours, especially purple. The alarm clock rang and Michel got up. 'You're awake early' he said. I acknowledged him, but didn't attempt to say anything else. I felt as though I was being influenced by some power. When Michel left I eventually went back to sleep. I woke with a definite voice I identified as my nan's, in my head saying, 'Now you can get up and go to him'.

Driving was difficult because of the operation, and when I arrived at the business it was eight o'clock. The last of the drivers was just pulling away. Michel was only just on his own, and the office staff was not due in for another hour. When I went inside he went ballistic. There was no happiness to see me, just anger. 'What are you doing here, go home. You should be in bed' he said. The hairs on the back of my neck stood on end, and there was that inner voice speaking to me, and now I was hearing it loud and clear. What was going on? 'Well I am here now so I might as well have a cup of tea', I said. He replied 'Well the phantom phone caller rings this time every day, and when I answer the phone goes down. I will make you tea and you can answer'.

My stomach turned, and when the telephone rang I picked up the receiver, but I remained silent. No one spoke on the other end, and eventually the phone went down. This happened three times, and Michel was pacing up and down, telling me to go home. I wouldn't let him near the telephone. I answered it when it rang for the fourth time and, although I remained silent a woman's voice said 'Michel is that you, can you speak now?', and I said 'No love this is Michel's partner, will I do?', and she put the telephone down. I stood and looked at him. I was engulfed by the most awful negative thoughts and emotions, but there was no way to express

67

them. I didn't want to shout or have any kind of a scene, but I felt very, very ill.

At that moment Nicola, who worked in the office, came in. Michel had to pull himself together, as he was crying. Nicola could see something was going on, and she put her arms around me and told me it was wonderful to have me back. She and I had become great friends during the three years she had worked for me. I went in to my office and called Michel in. 'Who is she?' I asked, and he immediately responded 'The woman from the estate agents that my brother is using to sell his house'. Michel's brother Paolo was now on his own, as his wife had died and they had no children. As a result of his wife's death and his own failing health, Paolo was selling their house and looking for a flat to buy.

Michel told me the woman's name was Angie, and he gave me her telephone number and I called her. A colleague answered the phone, and from her attitude I could see that Angie's colleague was aware of the situation. Angie didn't want to speak to me, but I told her colleague I would call to the office in person, as Angie could not escape me. When she eventually came to the telephone I said 'I would like to meet you and suggest you leave for the Post House Hotel now, as I am on my way'. She refused and said 'I can't just meet you, I am in work', and I said 'I'm sure you can think of an excuse to leave, you seem efficient in lying'. She tried to take control of the situation, saying she had done nothing wrong, but I was very forceful and told her if she didn't agree to meet me it would go badly for her. Michel let all this happen. He made no attempt to protect this woman, and I think he thought she could persuade me of their innocent relationship.

I left the office and drove to The Post House Hotel. I had no intention of causing a scene, but I hadn't known what was going on, and therefore felt powerless. I now wanted to empower myself. The woman was stood in the car park, drawing heavily on a cigarette. She was stood near the entrance to the hotel, and when I approached her she was furious. She started talking fast but I continued walking, and as I walked past her I said 'Coffee lounge, now. This is my show'. And she had to follow behind me, her high heeled shoes clip-clopping all the way.

I sat down in the coffee lounge and she joined me, and I had a good look at her. I said 'I wanted to see what you looked like, and to tell you our rubbish at home is collected on a Thursday. I will give Michel until Thursday to get out. He is rubbish and you are welcome to him'. She said 'Oh, don't be ridiculous, I never slept with him you know'. I said 'He suffers from premature ejaculation, and even if you had, you wouldn't have got a lot out of it', and we sat weighing each other up.

I asked her how it felt to be in possession of my rubbish, and she said she didn't want him. I asked her if she was married and she said 'Yes', did she have kids? 'Yes', did her husband know how she spent her time? 'No'. Where did she live, and she said 'I'm not telling you'. I told her, 'Give me twenty-four hours and I'll have that information, and I'll let you know I have it'. She was really worried and said 'What are you going to do?' and I told her 'How does it feel not to know? Well, hold that feeling because I've held it for a long time, and you helped in that'.

I got up to leave, and she said 'Is that it?' and I told her 'He has done this before; he is a serial adulterer who is emotionally immature. I'm not interested in the why, what or where, the fact that he has done it again is enough and I don't want to fight you because he is my leftovers, and you are welcome to him'.

It was obvious I had shocked her. I never once raised my voice, and I was proud of myself. In fact, when I got in my car I was laughing, thinking of what Michel's reaction would be if he knew what I had said to her. I recognised I had a really nasty side to my character, but I couldn't be sorry at that moment as I felt a little bit of self respect start to emerge. The laughter didn't last long, as then the pain set in, both emotionally and physically. However, I couldn't dissolve as I had given Angie a twenty-four hour deadline, and I was determined to come up with the goods. I would not ask Michel for her address, as he would be frightened of providing me with that information, in case I told her husband. I had no intention of doing so, but didn't want Michel or Angie to know that.

I had a friend who worked in another local estate agency, and I rang her. She didn't know Angie, but knew people who owned a shop next to where Angie worked. Give me a few minutes she said. She then rang me back and gave me Angie's full name and home telephone number. I rang the house. A man answered and I said 'Hello, you don't know me, but I am a friend of Angie's. I want to drop some makeup at your house as I'm in the area, can you give me the address please'. And he proceeded to give me the address. He then said 'Angie is here, would you like to speak to her?' She came to the telephone and I said 'Hi Angie, got you in two'.

I went home and crawled in to bed. I closed my eyes and there were beautiful colours on my eyelids, amazing purples and lime greens. I went to sleep watching these colours swirl and peak, back and forth, back and forth. Michel came home that evening, and had his brother with him. I knew his brother was there to smooth things over. Like Michel, Paolo had the gift of the gab and he thought he could win any woman over. I came down the stairs smiling and said, 'Hello, do you want a coffee?' and I made sure I kept smiling.

I made coffee for the three of us, and when we were seated I said 'How is the property search going Paolo?', and he said 'I'll have to find somewhere soon, as those stairs are a real problem for me'. I replied, 'Now don't worry, Michel is in close contact with your estate agents, and I am sure that between the two of them they will get things sorted'. I told them both to enjoy their coffee, and as I walked from the room my parting shot was 'Michel, back bedroom please, and I want you out by Thursday, on rubbish day'. It felt so good to do that. I felt like rubbish and I really wanted him to feel like rubbish as well.

Michel was so much like his brother, as his brother also had an eye for the ladies, and Paolo's wife had suffered because of it. In fact, within two weeks of her death, Paolo started courting her sister and he told me 'I married the wrong sister'. Six weeks after making that declaration, Paolo was in hospital with prostrate problems. He had an operation that wasn't successful, and it left him with an indwelling catheter attached to his private parts. I like to think his wife influenced this event, or at the very least was laughing about it, and it was surely another example of karma 'what goes around comes around'. I was revolted by him.

I went back to work the next day, and Nicola and I had a good talk. She was in a dreadful position, but put herself aside and told me exactly what had been going on. During my absence Angie had constantly been on the telephone to Michel. He would leave for long lunch hours, sometimes a whole afternoon, and he asked Nicola not to tell me these things. She had to take on extra tasks to make up for Michel's lack of commitment. Poor Nicola, I put my arms around her and cuddled her. She was such an emotionally delicate person, and was just coming to terms with problems in her past. She was quite distrustful of men because of her experiences and this was the last thing she needed. Michel knew this and he was also aware that he needed to be a good role model for Nicola. It was something he and I had discussed previously.

I couldn't take in how unprofessional, disloyal and immature Michel was. He was a liar and a cheat, and completely manipulative. What was wrong with me that I could take this person as my partner? I had to look at myself very closely. I had to acknowledge there was no one else to blame for the life I had led and the predicament I was in, but I knew I was changing and I was so glad of that.

So here I was with a stomach full of metal clips, but I was unable to rest. I knew I had to look after myself, but it was important to get things sorted. That evening Michel and I sat and talked. I emphasised he had to leave the house by Thursday; I no longer considered him my partner. He couldn't stop crying and begged me to give him another chance. He kept saying I had got everything wrong, and he was innocent. I felt the stirring of compassion for him. The more he talked, the more I lost my hard edge.

There was no way I would consider living with him, but I told him if he wanted to stay working in the business I would consider it, but it would depend on his behaviour. I said I was no longer willing to give him a 50% share in the business, but would consider a lesser percentage if he proved himself in the workplace. I stressed I would put up with no nonsense, and expected him to be professional in work, and respectful to me at all times. I in turn would give him the same respect. He sat and listened with tears running down his face. He said 'You don't have to do this; it doesn't have to be this way'. And I said 'A simple yes or no to my proposal will suffice'. I was hardening myself. This old fiddle was sick of being played.

I stayed at home and in bed for the next two days. Thursday came and I expected Michel to leave. He came home looking very unsure of himself, making no move to go. Kris knew exactly what was going on and he wanted Michel gone. He was now eighteen, and was disgusted with Michel. He called him Percy Perfect because of his pernickety ways around the house, and said his double standards were sickening. It was obvious Michel wasn't going to leave without pressure, so I told him he couldn't stay the night, and I asked him for his keys. He packed an overnight bag and before he left said to me 'If you need me I am at my brother's'. Was I supposed to call for him in a crisis? He was the crisis!

I went to work on Friday and Michel was sitting in the office wearing dark glasses. I was furious to see the drivers around him, patting his shoulder and offering support. As the drivers passed to get to their vehicles, they could barely conceal their feelings towards me. I was dismayed to realise Michel was crying, and obviously telling them he had been mistreated by me. He was enlisting the troops, gathering them to his side.

Later in the day I heard him talking on the telephone. He didn't realise I was there but was saying 'After all I've done for her, all the hard work I have put in, and she treats me like this'. He was also crying again. I looked on the caller display and realised he was talking to one of our regular female customers. This was the straw that broke the camel's back. My reputation among the staff and customers would be in tatters if he continued this behaviour. I felt so weak physically and should have been home recuperating but instead, here I was fire-fighting. However, he underestimated me because my hard side had lots of practice over the last few years. This side of me was now honed to perfection, and I had the potential to be lethal given the right set of circumstances, and these circumstances were just right.

That night I asked a locksmith to meet me at the work premises. I had him change all the locks. I also had him go to the house and change the house locks. My sister helped me collect every article of Michel's from the house, and we drove with his belongings to his brother's. I had Michel's wages, with a month's holiday pay and his P45 in an envelope, along with a sarcastic reference highlighting his weakness and betrayal. My sister and I emptied the car and when she knocked on the front door, Michel opened it. She pointed to his belongings in the front garden, and then handed him the envelope saying 'This is for you'. I went to the cash dispenser at our bank at five to twelve that night and drew out the maximum amount of money allowed for that day, once it was gone twelve I again drew out the maximum amount of money allowed. The next morning I was in the Bank as soon as they opened and I cleaned out any money left in our joint account.

I realised I should have severed all ties with Michel when I again found out what he was up to. I shouldn't have used a half-measure, which was giving way to my repeated pattern of weakness. I went to bed that night and was desolate. I couldn't stop crying. I felt so wounded, and wondered if I had physically harmed myself with all the stress and work while recovering from major surgery.

I was woken from sleep with a telephone on my eyelids. There was a cross over the telephone and inside my head the words 'Suffer it and grow' came. I was being told to stop weeping and wailing and looking to others for support. I had to go it alone and suffer the pain, in order to grow. In my head I said I understood, but asked for help with sleeping in the nights, as I was lying awake, and it was a torture. Every night after I had asked for help, I slept soundly. Every morning when I woke up I would say 'Thank you'.

The next couple of months were a haze. There was nothing but work and problems. I had to tell the staff my personal business, as they had a distorted view of the truth. I needed to enlist their help in keeping the business efficient and in profit. I promoted one of the drivers to Operations Manager, and he took over the front end of the business.

Shortly after Michel left I had a visit from my old neighbour Jo from Chepstow and she said to me 'At last you've got rid of the b------- have you?' I was shocked to hear her say this, and asked her why, and she said 'When you lived opposite us Michel used to come home in the lunch hours to walk Lucky. He started knocking at my door and, of course, Graham would be in work. The first time I called him in and made coffee. He flirted with me and I was so uncomfortable. The next time he called I told him I was busy and couldn't ask him in. He then started telephoning me, and eventually said he had fallen in love with me.' I was amazed and said 'Oh Jo why didn't you tell me?' and she said 'I couldn't Yve, I felt so awful about it. I did tell Graham though, I had to. Graham spoke to Michel and told him to stay away from me. Didn't you ever wonder why we had stopped socialising with you as a couple?' I thought about her questions and admitted that I had. I put a brave face on things while she was there but when she left I gave way to tears. My humiliation was complete.

I went to a solicitor to discuss my financial situation. He sent a letter to Michel to begin negotiations. Once things were stabilised I planned a holiday for Kris and me. My parents decided to join us, and we flew to Florida for two weeks. My mother's eldest sister May lived in Jacksonville with her husband Fred. We planned to visit her, and also visit with some of her children.

The holiday was brilliant and seeing our American family was lovely, and I forgot all the problems back home. The sense of freedom was heady, and a fabulous memory I have is driving along the sands at Coco Beach, with the Beach Boys blasting 'Surfing USA', and Kris and I singing and laughing. Another wonderful memory is being with my cousin Linda and her family at their ranch in Middleburg. They have a black creek running near their property, and a large tree had a rope tied to its branches. We would swing on that rope and drop in to the creek. The weather was lovely, and our screams echoed along the water. Kris also had a day surfing with his cousin Sean and Sean's mates. Returning home to the UK we were laden with luggage, as we had taken full advantage of the many shops.

Within two minutes of being in the house the telephone rang, and it was Michel. He wanted to know if we had a good holiday and said, 'Welcome home'. I was brought down to earth with a bang. Back at work the telephones were ringing, but not for business. Customers were cancelling our services. They all told the same story. They had been approached by a sales representative from a national carrier, and given a cheaper quote. This sales person knew the profile of our customer's freight and what I was charging them, and had cheaper quotes already prepared.

The recession had hit business hard, and no one could refuse the opportunity to save money. I lost forty per cent of my customer base within a week. It looked as though the business was finished, as I couldn't sustain those losses and didn't have the energy to fight back. Someone had given my customer base to the opposition. Welcome home indeed!

I thought back to my plea to the universe, when we were moving house. I had prayed 'If there is anyone there, please help me. If Michel ever betrays me again, please let me be in an emotional and financial position to stand on my own two feet, so that I can leave him behind'. It seemed that my plea was to be ignored, but I was willing to take responsibility for my actions. I knew I hadn't listened to that inner voice but, instead, had let my emotions rule me. It was unrealistic to expect the universe to save me.

Without the business I faced financial ruin, and there was more to come. In the post I had a letter from my solicitor telling me Michel was asking for the apportionment of the property, which was put in place when we bought our first property together, to be over-ruled. He also wanted a share of the business. I again put out a plea to the universe. 'Please help me. I'm frightened of life. I don't know who is listening to me, but I know you are there, and I am sorry that I've ignored you, but I'm ready to listen to you now'. I now had decisions to make regarding the business. I worked on financial projections, but the reality was, I needed a miracle.

Before I went to America I had been approached by an acquaintance of Michel's to quote for volume parcel freight. The friend was Lesley and he owned a household catalogue company. I rang Lesley and told him he needed to approach another company for the parcel work, as I was closing the business. He asked me why, and I told him. He then asked if I would drive over to see him, and this I did.

When I got to his offices, he was sat in the boardroom with the Finance and Sales Directors. I sat with them, and they asked a few questions. Lesley then made me the most amazing offer. He said I could move my business to his premises and I would pay no rent, electricity or rates. I could even have the use of his warehouse-men and equipment. He took me to a section of his large warehouse where offices sat empty, and he marked out an area in the warehouse that I could consider mine. I asked Lesley 'Why are you doing this?', and he replied 'Because I can'.

I agreed to his offer, and when I was driving from the meeting, I knew I had been given a miracle, and it was influenced by some higher power. Despite repeatedly not listening to my inner voice, my plea to the universe was being answered, and it seems I was being dealt with leniently.

In bed that night I dreamt I was at a fast flowing, wide river and I couldn't get across, although I knew that I had to. There was a man stood on the other side of the river, and he was familiar to me. He was calling for me to cross, and I was shaking my head. He pointed his hand at the water near me, and with a splash a sturdy stone appeared. He kept beckoning. Dubiously I stepped on to this stone, and again he was beckoning me. When I shook my head he raised his hand, pointed at the water and with a splash another stone appeared. I was gaining confidence and this continued until I was halfway across. Again he pointed at the water, I saw a splash but I couldn't see a stone.

He held his two hands towards me and had the most beautiful look on his face. I knew he was compelling me to have faith; he wouldn't let me sink. I turned and looked from where I had come, the stones that had led me had disappeared, there was no way back, I couldn't go back. He said 'If I give you the stones will you take the steps?', and I said 'Yes'. He said 'Sometimes you won't see the stones, will you still take the steps?' I looked around me and could see no other way out of my situation. I couldn't stay standing on a stone in the middle of a fast flowing river, frightened to take the next step and I couldn't go back. He looked so good and loving, I had no choice, and I said 'Yes'. I remember taking that step in to the unknown but didn't retain the rest of the dream.

I woke and it was a new day, suddenly I had faith. I was looking forward to organising the move for the business, and the hard work ahead was not daunting to me. The move went smoothly, and at last I could focus without overwhelming pressure. I was slowly rebuilding the business and my life. Michel was doing everything in his power to secure half the equity of the house, but this was 1993 and the housing market had crashed. Interest rates had rocketed, and there wasn't a lot of equity left in our house. He was also asking for money from the business. Even though he was fighting with me, he would still ring and cry and beg me to forgive him. I again spoke to the universe. 'Please help me secure our home so that Kris and I can stay living there.' And I had an inner knowing that things would work out. Yes, I had faith!

In work one day, a person came in to my mind who I hadn't spoken with for at least a year. This was a business acquaintance and, on an impulse, I dialled his number. We exchanged pleasantries and he said 'I was so sorry to hear of Michel's brother's death'. I asked 'When did he die?' He replied, 'Last week, and the funeral is tomorrow.' The death had not been in the local paper, and had I not made this call I probably wouldn't have found out. I knew I was influenced to make that call, and my heart was pounding. Michel was the main beneficiary of his brother's will. His financial status would change substantially and he would have no reason now not to pay towards the mortgage on our house, as well as other bills. This was another of those life-changing coincidences. Silently, in my head, I said 'Thank you'.

I was sorry that Michel's brother had died, but for my own purposes I had to let Michel know I knew. I rang him, he answered and I gave him my condolences. He was shocked and said 'How did you find out?' The tone of his voice was hostile; one day he had been begging, and now he was hostile. The reason for that was not hard to work out.

I rang my solicitor and told him the new development. He asked me 'What do you want to do?' and I said, 'I don't want any of Michel's money, but I want you to secure the house for Kris and me'. And so it was. Michel relinquished his share of the house, and the mortgage and title was signed over to me. He also stopped asking for any share of the business. I was free. The universe had answered, and when I looked at the sequence of events that had influenced and guided me, I was in awe. That night lying in bed I was treated to a light show. On my eyelids the colours tumbled from left right, bottom and top. They were psychedelic colours. I loved it and went to sleep smiling.

Shortly after this Michel left the UK and went to live in Italy, as his mother had moved back there after the death of her husband. He rang me the night before he left and he told me he was sorry for all that had happened and he wished me well. His words had a devastating effect on me. I was like a balloon that gets pricked by a pin. All the air left my body and I couldn't speak. The pain I felt was excruciating and everything seemed so utterly pointless. I couldn't cope with Michel's kindness, and the walls I had built came tumbling down.

Michel was shocked at my distress and kept saying 'I am sorry, I am sorry', over and over again. When I pulled myself together I was able to answer 'Its okay Michel, I couldn't have learned from a better b------ than you'.

Three

Building the faith

I had been taught so many lessons because of my dysfunctional behaviour, and my free will had led me to many painful places. I was desperate to grow and needed the help and support of the universe. I had to learn to trust and have faith.

My life revolved around work and home, and in my spare time I would visit with Kim and Chris. I would take Lucky with me and, together with their dog Silky, we would go for walks, or sit around the table, eating, drinking and talking about spiritual matters. Like me they were also getting spirit communication and had some crazy things happen.

For instance, their bedroom was on the first floor of their house and they had a balcony off the bedroom. On two occasions in the night they had fallen asleep and left their balcony doors open. This was quite a risky thing to do, as someone could have climbed on to the balcony and in to their bedroom. On both occasions they were woken by the telephone ringing and when they woke up and answered it, there would just be static on the line. Once awake, they would then notice the balcony doors were left open. On another two occasions they were woken up by a banging noise and they both witnessed the telephone rising up about seven inches, and banging down on the bedside table. They never felt frightened by these events but were comforted and happy to know there was someone with them.

I had started reading everything I could on this subject. One day I found an old spiritual book. In the book it explained when a medium is in training to work with spirit workers, those workers project visualisation on to the trainee's eyelids. The visualisation is to expand the vision, and peripheral vision of the third eye. It started with colour on the eyelids and then progressed to a square with images inside the square. It said that the square would get bigger and bigger. It mentioned the numbers, letters and faces that would tumble from left and right. It also mentioned the square with the little fat face in and it said this would occur at the end of the expansion. This was part of the making of a spiritual medium.

I couldn't believe what I was reading. This was the first time I had found any reference to the things that were happening to me. In my mind I said 'I want to work with you, show me how. I want to be a spiritual medium'. Within an hour of asking, I had my answer. Someone passed me a copy of the South Wales Echo. I opened it, and there in front of me was an article about a spiritual medium who was running a workshop locally. I said 'Okay I hear you. I will be there'.

I went to the workshop, and was glad to see the medium was a mature lady, who looked very normal. There were about twenty people there, both male and female, and all ages. She was talking about our sixth sense and how we could use it. She asked me to come to the front, and sat me on a chair with my back to the others. She told me someone would stand behind me, and I was to say what came in to my mind about that unknown person. Within minutes thoughts flooded in to my mind. It was a male that I sensed; he was tall and had a weakness in his chest. On and on the information came, and when I had finished everyone clapped. Apparently the man who stood behind me had been nodding in agreement to everything I said. I was astonished!

I began doing the trawl of development classes, but none of them seemed to explain the mechanics. I wanted to know how did it work, what was the purpose of our being here? I sat in these classes to develop my sixth sense, but didn't feel happy with them. We sat in a circle with our eyes closed, and were taught to link with spirit workers. We were encouraged to share our thoughts. Some people would breathe heavily, and start to talk with an accent. Another person might ramble on for what seemed like ages, and the words could be quite pious. Others became very emotional, and I would squint through my one eye to get a look at what was happening. I couldn't concentrate, and at times had to stop myself from laughing out loud.

How on earth did this fit in with real life? I was given differing information from group leaders regarding the person working with me. One leader said 'I see a native American Indian with you'. Another said, 'You have a monk'. I was even told a famous rock star was working with me. Needless to say, I didn't last long in these groups. Instead I asked in my mind, 'Please give me some practical and down-to-earth lessons', and left it to the universe to show me the way.

I had taken my sister to some of the development classes, and she decided to train as a healer. She joined a healing course run by the local Spiritualists National Union representative, and the course included practical and theory work. It was run from a building that was cold and neglected. My sister was talking to me one day. She mentioned she felt sorry for people who were ill going to that place for healing. Impulsively I said 'Why not hold the healing at our house? We have so much room and Kris and I are hardly ever there'. My sister thought it was a fantastic idea, but I said I would have to get Kris's approval before she put this to her tutor. I spoke to Kris and he said, 'As long as the spirits don't come in to my bedroom mum, then I am happy'.

The tutor was grateful to accept the offer and so it was, every Thursday evening, from six onwards, there would be a healing clinic at our home. Initially I said I wouldn't be involved, but circumstances conspired to pull me in and I found myself offering support to many of the people at the clinic. I had asked the spirit workers for practical and down-to-earth lessons, and that was what I got. I was working long hours at the business, and Kris was studying electronic engineering at Cardiff University. He would get home from University and organise the house ready for the clinic. The Healers would arrive at six and Kris would let them in, and then he would go out. I sometimes arrived home as late as eight and the clinic would still be going.

At one time, including the Healers, I counted thirty people in the house. This was made up of patients and their chaperones. A fantastic bond developed between those attending. Perhaps a wife would accompany a husband for healing, and after the healing they might stay for another cup of tea, as someone they had met at the clinic a couple of weeks before would be along soon. A few of my neighbours attended, and my next-door neighbour Hilary often used to help out, making tea and chatting with everyone. A friend of mine called Hazel had a superb library of spiritual books, and she set this up at my house, lending the books to anyone interested. These books became a talking point, and life after death was debated. There was a diverse mix of opinions, as well as of ailments among the patients.

We saw people with conditions such as skin rashes, migraine, gout, carpal tunnel syndrome, and arthritis. There were those with mental health problems such as stress and depression. We saw quite a few people who had suffered bereavement, with a few of them mourning the loss of a child, and then there were conditions such as cancer.

When I was in the house on my own, perhaps chilling out in the evenings, there would be so much activity it was amazing. A wall in my lounge used to emit loud banging noises. The strings on a guitar would play a note, pictures would move, lights would dim and the television had a mind of its own. Occasionally I would have a visitor with me, and I remember one of my visitors ran out through the front door, and told me she was frightened.

I am not a silly person, and realise you cannot attribute every happening to a spiritual event, but I would investigate all sorts of possibilities to rationally explain these things. But of course it wasn't just the physical happenings you had to take account of, it was also the feeling you would get of someone unseen being near you.

I woke up one night and thought I was having some kind of a fit. My body was bouncing from side to side. I was actually coming off the bed, and hitting my left side, then bouncing back to my right, then my left and so on. I went in to panic mode. I became aware of a man standing on the right side of me. He spoke to me mind to mind, he said 'It's okay, you have woken up too soon'. Immediately he said that I stopped panicking. I felt like a plane coming in to land, but the landing was bumpy. Slowly the bouncing became less violent, and then it gradually stopped. I looked, and the man had gone.

A couple called Elizabeth and Joseph visited the clinic. She was sixty-nine and he was seventy-one years of age. Elizabeth brought Joseph for healing, as he had Parkinson's disease. They were such lovely people, and used to make a point of waiting for me to come home so we could chat. They had five grown-up children, and lots of grandchildren. They would bring photos of their family, and were so proud of them. Their youngest child was Maureen and she and her husband were excitedly awaiting the arrival of their third baby, which was due in December, 1993. Everyone at the clinic would be told of the expected arrival and when Maureen gave birth to a beautiful baby girl, we all admired her baby picture.

Just after Christmas I was at home one evening and there was a banging on my front door. I was afraid to answer because I could hear sobbing. I asked who was there, but could hardly make out what was said. I opened the door to find Elizabeth, bent double and sobbing uncontrollably. I brought her in and she told me Maureen had died. Apparently she collapsed on Boxing Day, and died on New Year's Eve, she was thirty-two years old. It was believed part of the afterbirth had been left inside her, and she died of an embolism.

Elizabeth's grief was horrendous. I didn't know how to help her, and so I put my arms around her and held her close to me. I rocked her back and forth and let her cry. Maureen had left three children, a boy aged four-years, a girl aged two-years and the three-week-old baby. The shock of Maureen's death accelerated Joseph's illness, and he became bedridden. Maureen's husband had to continue working and although he employed a nanny, Elizabeth was helping with the three children. She still came to the healing clinic, but without Joseph. She was in such terrible pain, and had a desperate need for help.

On a Thursday evening Maureen's husband would go for counselling to help him with his grief. Elizabeth would look after the children for him and so she would arrive at the clinic about nine, after she had bathed and put the children to bed. She would be the last patient, and after she had healing the two of us would sit in the lounge. The fire and candles would be glowing, and Elizabeth and I would talk. She would pour out all her anguish to me, and I would tell her of my beliefs, trying to convince her that Maureen had survived bodily death. Elizabeth was very bitter at Maureen's death, and would tell me she didn't believe in an afterlife. I would gently explain to her the cryptic and subtle ways Maureen could communicate. I tried to encourage her to speak to Maureen in her head, and ask for help and guidance with the children.

One day Elizabeth told me all three of the children were crying, and she couldn't pacify them. She gave a plea to her daughter 'Where are you, I need your help', and she sensed Maureen's voice in her head, telling her to put the children in the car. Elizabeth did this and within minutes of starting off, all three were asleep. Whilst Elizabeth was telling me this, a picture of an orange cat fell off the wall. I put it back on its hook, and off it came again. I had a music tape playing quietly, and the tape itself stopped passing from spool to spool, but was spewing out of the cassette player. I said to

87

Elizabeth 'This is Maureen letting you know she is here. She wants to reassure you she has survived, and can be of help to you.' Elizabeth put her head in her hands and sobbed. She said to me 'But I want her here in the flesh, living with her children and husband, enjoying her life'.

The following Thursday, while I was driving home late from work, a thought came in to my head. It said 'My mother is tired and hasn't eaten all day, please prepare something for her'. I arrived at the house, and it was near nine pm. Most people had gone, but one of the healers was waiting for Elizabeth. She arrived shortly after me and was sent straight in to the healing room. I put a pizza in the oven, boiled some new potatoes and made a salad. I uncorked a bottle of red wine, and set the table for the two of us. After Elizabeth had her healing and once the healer left I sat her down. She said, 'How did you know I hadn't eaten?' and I said 'I didn't Elizabeth but Maureen knew, and she asked me to prepare something for you'. Elizabeth bowed her head and cried. When she composed herself I poured us both a glass of wine and we said a toast to Maureen.

Elizabeth and I kept in touch even after the healing clinic finished. Joseph died in July 1995, and I went to his funeral. Elizabeth was so devastated by previous events; she could barely take in that Joseph had gone. Shortly after his death, she told me she was in bed and felt Joseph snuggle up to her. Elizabeth said she asked Joseph to look after Maureen, and she felt a sense of love engulf her, which she took to be his response.

One morning Elizabeth got up early and was stood looking out at the back garden, thinking of Maureen. She quite clearly heard Maureen's voice greeting Elizabeth's next door neighbour. Maureen said 'Hello Terry'. Elizabeth knew the man next door had not been well, and she rushed to his house. His wife answered the door crying and said 'Terry has just died'. It was this final happening that gave Elizabeth acceptance that Maureen had survived. Elizabeth said to me 'I believe I was meant to bring Joseph to the healing clinic, but not for the reasons we thought. It was in preparation for Maureen's death, so I could be helped.'

Shortly after the healing clinic started, one night I got home from work and felt really weird about entering the sitting room. The hairs on the back of my neck were stood on end. I pushed open the door without entering the room, and everything seemed fine. I walked in and standing in the far corner was a man. He was dressed in a 1920s type of baggy suite, and was excessively thin. He looked as though he had consumption. I would put his age at about fifty-two. I stood frozen and looked at him, and he looked back at me, with a placid expression on his face.

I began to realise he was not absolutely solid. There was something about him that didn't seem right. I didn't feel threatened by him, just uncertain of his presence. He made no move and so I said 'If you've come for the healing, you have the wrong day'. His facial expression changed and he gave me a tolerant look, and the thought came in to my mind, 'You know I'm not here for that'.

Memories came flooding in; he was the man who was with me when I was four and came out of my body. He was also the man in my dream, helping me to cross the river. He was also the man at my right side when I was lying in bed and I thought I was having a fit, and he was telling me not to panic and saying I'd woken up too soon. I asked him 'Who are you? What's your name?' and he smiled. That smile conveyed to me his name wasn't important. I said 'If you won't tell me your name I'll call you HQ, as I know you are instructing me'. Slowly he faded and I was left looking at the blank wall.

This was a particularly busy time for me. I was constantly fire-fighting with the business. Lesley's help had been invaluable but I only stayed with him a year, as I knew it was not right to take advantage. As soon as I built the customer-base back up, I negotiated with a haulage broker to share their premises in a little Valleys town called Cilfynydd. We agreed on a fifty–fifty split of the overheads. I did a financial check on the broker's business, and was reassured they were financially sound.

I moved my operation to these new premises, and couldn't believe when within two months, the broker went bankrupt. I was now responsible for all the overheads. I had to look at bringing in extra work to cover these increased costs, but extra work meant extra staff, and so it went on, around and around.

I arranged to meet representatives of a company that was a management-buyout of a part of one of the old rail companies. They wanted me to deliver goods for them throughout South Wales. This could make a big difference to my situation. I was meeting them in a hotel in St Mellons, on the outskirts of Cardiff. As I was preparing to leave, Arthur, who was our old family friend from Llanrumney, kept coming to my mind. He and his wife Peggy had moved to Rumney, which is near St Mellons, and Arthur had recently died. Peggy was suffering with cancer.

I was driving to my meeting, and Arthur wouldn't get out of my head. In the meeting I needed a good deal of concentration. There was an accountant present and he was going over figures, working out vehicle capacities and so on, and I needed to keep up with events. Arthur wouldn't leave me alone, and so I said in my head 'Arthur I hear you and I believe you want me to go to Peggy. When the meeting is finished, I will go straight there. I am on a tight time frame, as I have another meeting back at the office and so you will have to delay those attending, so I don't keep them waiting'. That was obviously what Arthur wanted to hear, as I then had full concentration. When the meeting finished I went straight to Peggy. She answered the door and said, 'Yvonne, God has answered my prayers, you've been sent to me'. She put her hand in her pocket, and brought out a plastic bag full of her hair.

She was having chemotherapy for the cancer, and woke up that morning with a bald head. She and my mum had been shopping and bought her a wig in case this happened. She had the wig on, but hadn't placed it properly. She was upset and said she was never going out again. I sat her down and looked at the wig, but it was very complicated, as there were strings and a pulley system. I rang the shop that sold the wig, and they talked me through the process of fitting it properly. She looked good in it, and I rang my mum and told her what had happened. She sent my father to pick up Peggy, and I was able to drive back to work. I was three-quarters of an hour late for my meeting, but the people attending had been delayed and arrived a quarter of an hour after me. Arthur didn't let me down.

I was so pleased to be working with HQ, life took on a completely different meaning. I loved helping and giving, it was so satisfying. There was such wonderful work being done at the clinic and I was meeting fabulous people, such as Mel. He was thirty-eight years of age and dying from a brain tumour. Mel was a businessman, he ran an off-licence shop. He was married to Kath, who already had two children when they met, and she and Mel went on to have another two children. Mel was diagnosed with a brain tumour when he was thirty-six. He had surgery twice, as well as chemotherapy, but after two years he was eventually told nothing more could be done for him and was sent home to die.

His wife bought a new television for Mel to enjoy. For some reason it wouldn't work and they thought the aerial might be at fault. They rang a local aerial company, and a man called Dave, who coincidentally was a friend of mine, visited the house. He went to the television, turned it on and it worked perfectly. Kath and Mel couldn't believe it, as it was definitely not working before. Dave spoke to Mel 'What's the matter with you mate?' and Mel said he had been sent home from the hospital to die. Dave told the couple he believed the reason he had to visit their home was to tell them of the healing clinic at my house. Even though Dave hadn't contacted me about this event, the next Thursday I was home early and a four-by-four vehicle pulled on to the drive. A lady helped a man out; the man was supported by a zimmer frame. Mel had found his way to us!

My sister Gail was assigned as Mel's healer, and week by week she worked with him. Within four weeks he came to the clinic without a need for the frame. He reported he was feeling so much better and, as a result of this, he was going to the hospital for a blood platelet count. He had even been back in work for a few mornings. The following week he told us the hospital were astonished to find an increase in his blood platelets, and as a result of this he was booked for further chemotherapy. The next week he turned up at the clinic carrying a bowl, as he was so very sick because of the chemotherapy.

Everyone at the clinic loved him, he was such a kind man and he had amazing brown eyes. He had so much to live for and his concern was for his wife and children, he didn't want to leave them on their own. Even though he was feeling so sick, he had us all laughing. Apparently his wife Kath wanted to have another baby by him, and he had us in hysterics telling his reaction to this, or rather his lack of reaction.

The following week we were dismayed to see he was back using the zimmer frame. We had acquired a copy of the song 'All that she wants is another baby' and we opened the door to him, with the music blasting and a few of us dancing and singing the words to him. He stood on the drive, leaning on his frame, laughing. I treasure that memory.

Mel went downhill rapidly, and eventually was bedridden. My sister would call at his house to give him healing twice every day, once on her way home from work, and again before he went to sleep for the night. He said the healing was better than the morphine drip he used. On his visits to the healing clinic, he and I had sat together talking about the afterlife, and he knew I believed we survived bodily death. Mel didn't believe in an afterlife but, because of his situation he wanted to believe, and was looking for proof. In the last few weeks of his life he began to see spirit people at the end of his bed. They were family members who had died. He would tell my sister about this when she sat at his bedside.

The day came when my sister rang me and asked if I wanted to say goodbye to Mel. I left for his house immediately. He was lying in the bed snoring gently. I sat at his side and held his hand. I told him I was there. He woke and I said to him 'Mel, can you see the light with the people stood waiting?' and he said 'Yes I can, they are there'. I said 'Mel, please go to the light and be with your people', and he said 'No, I can't, I'm afraid'. I said 'There's no need to be afraid babe; it's like going from one room to another'. He squeezed my hand and fell back in to sleep. I kissed him and left. He died that evening. His wife was playing Whitney Houston's song, 'I will Always Love You'. She said he gave a big sigh, and just stopped breathing.

The funeral was to take place in a little village, near to Mel's business. My sister was leaving work to attend. She and I were meeting in the Church. She had to cross from one end of Cardiff to the other, and plotted a route for herself, but got lost. She had no recollection of taking a wrong turn, and was annoyed with herself for such a lapse in concentration. She was desperately working out in her mind how to get back on route. She noticed a funeral car in front of her, and acknowledged it must be a day for funerals. She then became aware the funeral car was travelling in the same direction as her. The penny then dropped. It was Mel; he was making sure she was with him to the bitter end.

I was stood in front of the Church and saw Mel arrive, with my sister following behind. When she told me what had happened I felt so pleased she had accompanied him. The Church was beautiful, and very atmospheric. At the end of the service the same Whitney Houston song was played, and just as her voice was soaring, the sun shone through the stained glass windows. We were bathed in wonderful light. Gail and I went to the graveyard and as I looked around, I was amazed to see the grave of Peggy's husband Arthur. Mel was to lie opposite Arthur and it seemed to me Arthur was returning a favour. It was karma, 'What goes around comes around'. We knew Mel would be well looked after.

One Thursday, about six weeks after Mel's death, Gail came out of the healing room and said 'Mel is back, he was just stood at the side of me while I was giving healing'. As she said this, we saw Mel's wife Kath arrive in her car. We had not seen her since the funeral. She had come to give money collected in Mel's memory. She wanted us to buy new hand-towels for the clinic.

One Wednesday night, two of the healers rang me to say they couldn't make clinic the next day. That meant only two healers would be working, and I knew it was going to be a busy night. I was so worn down with work, and felt on the verge of collapse under the pressure. This was all I needed. I felt angry with HQ and spoke to him, saying 'How do you expect me to cope with this? I can't just pull healers' out of nowhere, so it's over to you. You had better get it sorted'.

I went to bed crying and apologised to HQ. I told him I was buckling under the strain. I knew the business was important, as it funded not only Kris and me, but also the healing clinic. I needed help with the business and I was also lonely. I asked HQ to send me a man who would be like a soul mate to me. I asked for someone who would help me on all levels.

Thursday morning came and I was back feeling angry. I was in work for six and was already encountering problems, as two people hadn't turned up. At every available moment I was speaking to HQ in my head. I told him there was no way I was going home that night unless he got things sorted. I knew if there were only two healers' working, there would be a back log of people when I got home. I was just too weary to be bothered.

I employed fifteen people in the business, and there were always problems. The staff knew I had a sympathetic nature, and quite often they took advantage of this. I was constantly fire-fighting. Any problems the staff had, they quickly became my problems, and I was always doing over and above what could normally be expected, and I was suffering because of this. I had no lunch hour that day, and by two in the afternoon felt my head was exploding. I needed to get out for ten minutes. I drove my car aimlessly, not knowing where I was going. I found myself in the shopping area of a place called Aberdare.

I stopped the car and looked around me, and noticed I was opposite a new-age shop. I got out of the car and approached the shop. I opened the door and went to the counter. There was a sign advertising healing. A very attractive, older lady appeared from behind a curtain and I said 'Who is the healer?' and she said 'I am, and my name is

Trish'. I said 'Look this may seem weird, but there is a healing clinic every Thursday evening at my home in Cardiff and healers work there on a voluntary basis. There will be a lot of people there tonight, and two of the healer's can't make it. Would you consider coming?' She immediately said 'Yes, write your details down and tell me what time to be there'. I left the shop feeling overawed at this power which could influence events so easily, and I also felt incredibly humble. Driving back to work I said to HQ, 'I want to thank you for working with me, and I want you to know that my faith is building'.

Three days later I met a man who I believed was my soul mate, sent to me by HQ in answer to my plea. His name was Jeff, and he was connected to one of my customers. I was asked by this customer to partner Jeff at a dinner party but I declined as I was too shy to do this, but the next day Jeff rang me. He invited me to a dinner for just me and him at his house, which was directly around the corner from my home. I went and had a lovely time.

Jeff was originally from Cardiff but had been living and working in Ireland for a number of years. He was a successful business man but had divorced and then sold his profitable company and returned to his roots in Cardiff. He was renting the house near me whilst looking for a permanent place to buy. The customer who introduced us was living with Jeff's eldest daughter. Jeff was very laid back, and was like an old hippy, but he was an extremely astute business man. He would discuss my financial problems with me, and understood that the recession had a devastating effect on businesses, particularly those in the service industry.

Jeff was also interested in the healing, and asked if he could come to the clinic. He was amazed at the work being done there. My sister explained how healing worked and Jeff asked if he could have a go. She helped him link with the healing source, and I found him a volunteer patient. This experience freaked Jeff out. He said he saw an image of the patient's body on his eyelids, like an x-ray but in colour. That was too strange for him to deal with.

A few nights later Jeff was at home in bed, and he saw three people standing at the bottom of the bed. They were two men and one woman. The woman spoke to him and said 'We are going to take your progression very slowly'. He rang me immediately and woke me up. He was incredulous that he should have this experience. Another time he felt a woman get in his bed, and the feeling she brought was of pure love. Jeff was a bit frightened of these happenings.

My animals, Blue the cat, and Lucky the dog, loved the healing clinic. Everyone made such a fuss of them. However, they were getting old. I used to take Lucky to work with me, and now she wasn't fit enough. While I was in work, my father went to my house every day to walk her, and he always made a fuss of Blue as well. Once Blue realised his visit was a daily event, he would sit at the top of our road and wait for my father.

I used to say to HQ 'Please don't let my animals die when I'm away from them'. At Easter 1995, I was at home and Blue was obviously very ill. He was not a lap cat, but he got on to my lap and looked me in the eyes. I swear he was telling me goodbye. I called my vet and he came to the house. Blue was about nineteen years of age, and apparently his kidneys had stopped functioning. The vet gave him an injection to put him to sleep, and I was able to hold him in my arms whilst this was being done. In my mind I begged HQ to ask my Uncle Jim, who was an animal lover, to collect Blue. I cried buckets, and Kris and Lucky cried as well.

I never realised how much Lucky relied on Blue. If someone knocked at the door, Lucky no longer responded. When Blue was alive, if someone knocked on the door he would run to see who it was, and Lucky would be alerted to the fact someone was there. It was now evident Lucky was quite deaf. Four months after Blue died, Lucky and I were sleeping in my bedroom one night, and she woke me up. It was excessively warm in the room and Lucky and I went and sat out in the back garden. It was magical. We cuddled up and I talked to her. I told her I loved her and she would always be with me. We went back to bed and she woke me again at about five. She had collapsed on the floor and her eyes were spinning around. I knelt by her side and spoke to her and she was able to wag her tail. I called the vet and he came immediately. He said Lucky had a stroke. It was up to me whether I wanted her put to sleep, or I could wait and see what happened, but he couldn't guarantee anything.

She was eleven years of age and I didn't want her to go, but I knew HQ had arranged for me to be with her when she had the stroke. If it had been an hour later, I would have left for work. In my mind again I spoke to HQ, please let my Uncle Jim and Blue be there to meet Lucky. As I did with Blue, I held Lucky when she had the injection and took her last breath. I was inconsolable but, at the same time, I knew HQ had given us all a wonderful gift. I had been with my animals at the end. Over the next few weeks I kept saying to HQ 'Are they okay, can they visit me yet?' and I realised I was very demanding, but I couldn't help myself. I needed to know they had survived.

After about eight weeks, I was lying in bed at night and I heard the familiar sound of Lucky running up the stairs. She ran in to my room, and I felt her two front legs land on the bed. I then heard and felt her back legs scrabbling for leverage and, thump, her whole body landed. Then I heard the patter of Blue's little paws. Up the stairs and into the room he came and, with a jump, he landed on the bed. This was a familiar ritual, played out every night when they were alive. I lay there and in my mind I told them I loved them, and one day would be with them. I thanked HQ for giving me such an amazing experience.

In late 1995 I started having a feeling of unease regarding our home, and kept having thoughts of moving. I said to HQ 'I think you are influencing me to sell the house. I'll put it in the hands of an estate agent but, I know if I've got it wrong and you don't want me to sell, then no one will want to buy it'.

The agent came, and I was in the kitchen making tea while she was looking around the house. She came in to the kitchen and said to me 'Do you have a big black dog?' I said 'I did, but she died recently', the lady was really embarrassed. She said she realised it was the spirit of a dog she was seeing, but she didn't usually share these experiences with anyone. I laughed and told her the house was used for spiritual healing, and I was well used to spiritual happenings. She told me she saw my Lucky sitting on the settee, and looking out of the lounge window. Lucky always sat there and loved to see what was happening in the road. I felt this was confirmation from HQ regarding selling the house. It was a spiritual link.

A few days later the agent rang me. She told me she had sent a photographer to take photos of the outside of the house. She asked if anyone had been home when he took the photos and I told her 'No, Kris and I are out early every day'. She said there were people visible in my bedroom window, and the central figure was a lady holding what looked like a scroll in her hand. She promised to post the photo to me so I could see for myself. When the photo came I couldn't believe it. She was right. There were people clearly visible in my bedroom window, and there was the lady with a scroll-like object in her hand.

One night my neighbour Hilary knocked on my door. She had a friend with her who was crying bitterly. Hilary said, 'I hope you don't mind, but this is my friend Gina. She is terribly upset, and I don't know what to do with her'. I said to Gina, 'Oh, you poor thing, what on earth is the matter?' Gina was sobbing, and said her husband had left her for a young woman. She had just discovered all his family were aware of the affair, and had entertained them as a couple. She felt his family were approving of the situation.

I called them in, but before we made it to the lounge, a thought voice came in to my head and said 'My name is Violet, but you can call me Vi, and I certainly do not approve'. Without thinking I repeated this to Gina, and she stopped crying, looked at Hilary and said to her 'How does she know that?' Apparently Violet was Gina's dead mother-in-law. I was as amazed as Hilary and Gina. Speaking my thoughts had just happened; it was a completely spontaneous thing. Hilary made tea while I sat and talked to Gina. Vi gave her wonderful evidence of survival, along with words of wisdom. When they left my home Gina was calm. Wow, to me what had happened was mind-blowing. I loved it, and told HQ I wanted to do more of this kind of work.

A week later Gina came back, and asked me if I could contact Vi again. I concentrated and said, 'I can't seem to do that, but the name Mary is going over and over in my head'. I gave certain information to Gina, but she said, 'That sounds like you are speaking to Vi'. 'Well I can't claim that, as the information is associated with Mary' I said. When Gina went home she felt drawn to look in an old bureau draw. She found documentation belonging to Vi, and her second name was Mary.

Gina started attending the healing clinic. One night she brought her young son Matthew, who was about eleven at the time. He was waiting for his mother in the sitting room. I gave him a cuddle, and he pointed to an empty chair opposite. He said 'Who has been sitting in that chair?' and I asked 'Why love?' Matthew said 'They have left a dark green', 'What do you mean?' I said. 'The dark green is all over the chair', he said.

I had just been learning about aura colours, and knew dark green was associated with negativity. The person who had recently vacated the chair was an extremely negative person. 'Do you see colours?' I asked him. 'Oh yes, all the time' he said. I pointed to another chair, which had recently been vacated by an emotionally upset lady. I asked him 'Is there a colour left on that chair?' 'Oh, yes, that person has left lots of red behind' he said, and he was right, red is the colour associated with emotional imbalance. I asked him if he had any other strange happenings. He said, 'Before I go to sleep at night an old man appears at my bedside. He has long flowing clothes, and long, grey, curly hair. He brings a big leather-bound book with him. He sits on my bed, opens the book and reads to me. Eventually I fall to sleep and I never remember what he's read to me when I wake'.

I knew Matthew had suffered immensely over the break-up of his family. He seemed to have been overlooked in the emotional turmoil and fighting between the warring parents. I said to Matthew 'This man is a very special person, and he is there for you. While all this conflict is going on around you, he will be with you. You must be a very special little boy Matthew for this man to have chosen you.' There seemed no end of the magic from the spirit world, and I was so glad Matthew was receiving their help. I often think about him and wonder if he has developed his wonderful gift.

While all these events were happening in the healing clinic and my personal life, the business was absolutely manic. I had secured the work with the management-buyout company, and the increased volumes this brought meant we were working to capacity. I had taken on two extra employees to help service this increase.

The first two months of working with them gave me severe cash-flow problems. I was like a juggler, trying to keep all the balls in the air. In the transport industry you have to give the customers credit, and thirty days credit is normal. I had carried out financial checks on this company, and their bank gave a good reference. We did ten weeks work for them and received no money. I was constantly on the phone, threatening to withhold their goods. In the end I drove to their headquarters in Birmingham. I was devastated to be told they had gone into liquidation. All the money we had worked so hard for was gone. This amounted to £55,000, but I also had to pay the costs incurred for servicing their work, and this was probably around £27,500. Out came the calculator and, once again, I was punching in figures, adding up overheads and making projections for income. I needed to reduce the workforce, and reduce overheads. Moving business premises was a must, and so I set about finding an alternative.

There was a local haulier who used our service. I was speaking to him, and he said there was a vacant warehouse and offices on his site. He took me to view it, but the interior was in a poor condition, and I was worried about health and safety. He said he would get builders in to put the premises right. It was in his interest to have us on site, as he could pass more freight to us, which would save him costs.

We did a deal and it meant I could halve my overheads. He promised to get builders in and he gave me a moving date. I got regular progress reports from him and, on his say-so, I gave notice to our landlord and organised switching utilities and so on. I had not been back to the premises to see progress for myself, as having reduced the staff; it meant I was needed in the office.

We moved on a Wednesday evening, and all the staff stayed to help. We filled two forty-foot trailers with our belongings, and set off for the new premises. When we arrived I couldn't believe my eyes. I had been deceived. The premises hadn't been touched. Toilets were not working, plug sockets were unsafe and there was rubble and litter lying around. Even if I could have overcome these obstacles it would have been foolhardy to put any trust in the individual involved. I could not do business with him. There was no point in unloading the vehicles.

I found a quiet corner and spoke to HQ. 'I believe you are telling me to stop the business', I said 'How can I stop, people are relying on me, how will they manage, and what about me? I won't be able to pay my mortgage and what about the clinic? Also I'll owe people money, what about them?' The list of problems seemed endless, but I had the sense that HQ was holding out his hands to me, showing me that if I couldn't see the stone, I could still take the step. It was the ultimate test of my faith in him and, just as the dream had shown me, there was no going back.

Jeff had helped with the move and I spoke to him and said 'That's it; I'm closing the business'. He said 'Look Yve, you don't have to do that, we can go back to the old premises and unload everything, and sort out the landlord tomorrow'. I said 'No, I can't go back', that was it, and I was done, I was taking a step without knowing where I would land.

We parked the trailers at the old premises and went home. I sat in my lounge and was in shock. I was asking HQ 'What am I going to do?' Loaded on the two trailers were all the goods to be delivered the next day. I couldn't let people down. Into my mind came thoughts of two men who operated the same business as me, but in Newport, which is a town next to Cardiff. I rang them and told them my situation. I said 'If I give you my customer base you could take over my business, but you have to take my staff as well'. They jumped at the opportunity. I made arrangements for them to collect the goods that night, and I also rang around the staff telling them of my decision to close, but offering them the opportunity of employment with the new company in Newport.

So that was it, overnight the business had gone. I hadn't prepared for this, and didn't have money to pay my household bills for that month, let alone the next month. I spoke in my mind to HQ and reminded him of my dream. I told him 'You had better make sure I don't get wet!' The next day was Thursday. I was there to greet the healers, and explain what I'd done. We waited for patients to arrive, and not one turned up. That was really amazing because the clinic had been so busy. We sat in the lounge and everyone agreed 'That's it; the clinic is closed'. We wrote to the patients telling them, and giving an alternative venue for them to receive healing.

The healers tutor was called John. He was a tall, dignified-looking man in his seventies. His wife was Joyce and, although she wasn't involved at the clinic, she and I had just started to get to know one and other. Joyce was a Spiritual Medium and Teacher. When the Healers left I called Joyce and poured out my fear to her. She was wonderful to me, and I kept her on the telephone for ages. I told her of the photo of the house the estate agent had given to me, and she asked to see it. I sent it to her, and she told me the people were spirit workers, and the lady was holding plans in her hand, and these plans were for me. She said I was in service to spirit and the universe, and I was not to be afraid, as those who worked with me would never let me down. That picture and Joyce's explanation were absolutely mind-blowing to me. I knew HQ was behind all these happenings, and now he had given me physical proof there was a plan and a purpose to my life.

Jeff was also a tower of strength. I had started the business operating as a sole trader, but had switched in the last two years to a limited company. I put the company in to voluntary liquidation, and the tax man sent me a bill for £33,000. I was horrified at this, and knew it couldn't be right. My accountant was insistent it was right. Jeff went through approximately five years of my accounts and found a major error. In the year of the switch from sole trader to limited company, creditors had been heavily understated, and this made it look as though I had made large profits. The tax man reassessed my obligation and my tax bill was reduced to £8,000. What a relief!

For the first three weeks of the business closure I hadn't signed on for benefits, and didn't want to. I was kidding myself I would get a job, but the reality was I had burned out. Jeff pressured me to get an appointment with the Benefits Agency and reluctantly I did this. At the appointment the clerk told me I was extremely lucky, as I was eligible to have the interest on my mortgage paid but, if I had come a day later, the rules would have changed. I would have had to wait nine months before receiving the first interest payment. I thought these happenings were really incredible, I had taken a step without knowing how I would land, and HQ had not let me fall, I was protected.

My life was now such a contrast to how it had been. I didn't need to get up in the morning, and the animals weren't around to enjoy this time with me. Kris was twenty and was in University in Cardiff, and very much had his own life. I spent a lot of my time with Jeff at the house he had bought. I had given up smoking twelve years before, but found myself starting to smoke again, and I was also drinking alcohol quite a bit. I felt I was doing what normal people did, and was really enjoying myself.

The house was still for sale, but there was little interest in it, and I was happy to let things drift along. However, Jeff was getting itchy feet, and he decided it was time for an adventure. In February, 1996 Jeff decided he was going to live in Spain. He asked me to go with him. He painted a wonderful picture of us living an idyllic life. I discussed this with Kris and, although he was still living at home, he was thinking of moving out. He would be able to come back and forth to me for holidays, and when he finished his degree in electronic engineering, he might even come and live there. Jeff told him there would be plenty of opportunities to work with electronics on boats, which being a typical Pisces was a passion of Kris's. Kris was quite excited by this.

I agreed to go with Jeff, and he put his house up for sale immediately. I spoke to HQ and said 'If this move to Spain is in the plan for my life, then it will happen. If it is not in the plan, then it won't. I am happy for you to influence events'. Jeff took me on a couple of holidays to Spain to look around for a suitable place. We couldn't believe it when he got a buyer for his house straight away, while mine just sat there. At this time Jeff's eldest son Connor was living with Jeff. It was agreed Connor would come with us on our adventure, and Jeff and I flew to Malaga to find a flat in Marbella for Jeff and Connor to rent. They could then set about finding the right property for Jeff to buy.

My old friends Shirley and Tony had left the UK a few years previously, and they were living in Marbella. It was Kim and Chris's intention to also move there. This was the reason we chose Marbella. We found the perfect flat in a beautiful marina, and everything was arranged. Jeff and Connor were able to leave for Spain in May, while I organised the sale of Jeff's house. After a few weeks Jeff started calling me, saying he was anxious for me to join him. There was nothing I could do, my house hadn't sold, and that was that. I flew to Spain in August for another holiday with Jeff, and he was so attentive to me. I felt confused to realise he seemed to have marriage on his mind, as he kept making hints such as 'Yve you could get married in those shoes', or 'Yve, what is your ring size?' I didn't respond to these comments, as I wasn't comfortable with them. He wasn't saying anything clearly and I was too embarrassed to ask him what he meant. It just was not a comfortable subject.

I felt sad when I left Jeff, as I had a feeling it was the last time we would be together as a couple. I tried to explore where these thoughts were coming from, and told myself not to be silly. Once I was back home, Jeff called me daily to say he was missing me and he complained that, had he realised he would be in Spain for such a long period of time without me, he would never have left Cardiff. He told me he only left for Spain before me because Connor was anxious to start the adventure, but he had quickly established a circle of friends, and Jeff was now left on his own. Eventually he said if I wasn't going to join him, he was coming back.

Kris had moved in to rented accommodation with some friends, and so I was in the same position as Jeff, and was on my own. I told him he and Connor could stay with me when they came back. Then a miracle happened, I got an offer on the house. The offer was not as good as I had hoped for, and I discussed it with Jeff. I told him I was willing to let the house go, so we could start our adventure together. He didn't act particularly enthusiastic at my news. This was confusing to me, as I assumed he would be thrilled at this turn of events. When he rang the next day he was more responsive, and I rang the agent and accepted the offer.

Over the next few days Jeff would ring, but he was quite cool. The note of desperation had left his voice. I sensed some kind of battle was taking place within him. Meanwhile, a surveyor came to the house and did a full structural survey on behalf of the buyer. One day Jeff rang, and he sounded paranoid. He asked me if I was trying to get him to marry me. I couldn't believe what he was saying, and laughed out loud. It was he who had been hinting about marriage, whilst I had been ignoring his hints. He had set the pace for our relationship and with my track record, there was no way I would be doing anything I wasn't one hundred percent certain of. Also, having married once in my life already, I was determined I would never marry again. I was offended by Jeff's question, and told him to forget the whole thing. I would not be coming over to Spain. He tried to back pedal, but I was having none of it. I was starting to understand that I deserved better treatment than this.

That afternoon the estate agent rang and said my buyer wanted a further reduction on the house, as the survey had shown some areas of concern. I said to tell the buyer I was not interested and to forget the sale. She told me not to be hasty, as they might go ahead at the agreed price, but there was no need for me to sell the house at a lower price now. I realised once again HQ had influenced events, and it seemed as though Jeff's hand had been forced, and he had revealed a side of himself that wasn't attractive to me. I was gutted as I truly did love Jeff, but not enough to make another mistake. I had thought he was my soul mate, and that evening I cried to HQ saying, 'Why did you let me think he was for me?'

I went to bed in my lonely house and, as I snuggled under the blankets, I heard a loud crash coming from the direction of the downstairs hallway. Someone must have broken in, there was no other explanation. I couldn't understand why the burglar alarm hadn't gone off, and then thought perhaps I hadn't set it. I picked up the telephone and dialled the emergency police number. I told them I was in the house on my own, and I thought there was an intruder. They said they would be there immediately. I opened my curtains and looked out the front window. I saw four police cars pull on to my drive. Police jumped out, and they ran around the sides and back of the house. I opened my bedroom window, and a policeman asked me to open the front door. I told him I was frightened to come down the stairs, and threw my keys to him. I heard him open the front door, and my burglar alarm started to beep. I ran down the stairs to turn it off.

In the hallway I had a basket of artificial ivy trailing down the wall, which was as light as a feather. The basket of ivy was off the wall and lay diagonally across the hallway, as though staged. The policeman stood looking at me and said 'What's happened here?' I had no explanation and thought 'He must think I'm crazy, or perhaps attention seeking'. If the basket of ivy had fallen off the wall, it would have landed in a heap and, as it was so light it certainly wouldn't make the crash I heard. 'There must be someone in the house' I said, and so the policemen looked around. 'There's no one here love, and in any case you had the alarm on. If there was anyone walking around downstairs, the alarm would have detected them' I was told. I apologised for wasting their time, and they told me I was to call them again if I was worried. They left, and I re-set the alarm and went back to bed thinking, 'What on earth was that all about?' HQ was silent, and eventually I went to sleep.

The next day I rang Joyce, and told her what had happened with Jeff. I also told her of the strange event in the night, which prompted me to call the police. I asked her what she thought it all meant. She told me 'You have received symbolic communication from those in spirit. They have used the artificial ivy to tell you it wasn't the real thing with Jeff, he was a plant'. 'You mean they are telling me Jeff was sent to me, but not as my soul mate?' 'Yes, exactly', said Joyce, 'He was a plant and not the real thing at all.'

Even though I was upset I couldn't stop laughing, I told Joyce in the night I had cried to HQ 'Why did you let me think he was for me?' I had to admit meeting Jeff had helped me sort business problems. He had saved me a lot of money with the tax man, and had encouraged me to sign on for benefits. I felt humble to realise how well I was protected.

I was fascinated to learn about symbols, and Joyce told me they were a universal language. We receive spiritual guidance in our sleep state by way of symbolic dreams, and as demonstrated to me by the ivy incident, we were also given symbols in our waking hours. I had to learn this universal language, and I told Joyce this and she promised to teach me.

Four

In training

Once I had faith I then had to work hard at communication. I needed to understand the cryptic and subtle language of the universe.

I began attending a class at John and Joyce's house, and everything she taught made absolute sense. In fact, some of what she taught me I already knew, and the pieces of the puzzle were starting to fit together. On many, many occasions previously when waking from sleep I was aware I had information running through my mind. When this filtering of information happened I couldn't quite grasp what it meant. Now I knew, as all the information I had received was flooding back, as though Joyce had released a damn. Joyce told us our spirit is separate to our body, and without the spirit, there could be no life or animation in our body. She also said in our sleep state sometimes the spirit leaves the body, and we are taking for guidance to the astral plane.

I thought back to my sleep paralysis incidents that had reoccurred throughout my life. The thought came in to my mind 'I had woken up too soon'. I voiced this to Joyce and she said 'Yes, undoubtedly that's the answer, your spirit was not properly in your body and, therefore you couldn't move'. 'Also I had a sense there was someone with me' I said. 'Oh, there is someone from the spirit world with you.' said Joyce, 'They make sure no harm comes to the body while you are away. Your spirit is also escorted by another spirit worker, and so there are usually two spirit people involved in the process.' I told her about the thumping and whooshing noise I had experienced and she explained 'When the spirit is out of the body your senses can be heightened. You were hearing your heart beat and the blood circulating around the body.'

That made so much sense. I remembered when I was four and HQ was escorting me back to my body, I also thought back to the time I had woken and thought I was having a fit, and HQ told me I had woken too soon. I could so easily understand what Joyce was teaching me, as I had experienced so many things. How many people were there experiencing these various stages of the spirit leaving the body? I thought of my mother and her distress at the sleep paralysis. She had gone the medical route, and had been seeing a psychiatrist for a while. No amount of medication had stopped her having this experience.

In Joyce's classes we discussed the cryptic and subtle ways spirits can communicate with us. Joyce said when we die and go to the astral plane, we have healing and our mind is unlocked. The power of the unlocked mind is incredible, and it is this power that could make objects move, interfere with electrics, influence people by putting thoughts in their minds, and make coincidences happen. She explained the spirits with the unlocked minds could only come back to earth in service to the universe and, therefore, were only here for the good.

All the experiences I had over the years were now understandable to me. I began to see people's auras. I would see the life force around them, like a very light pencil outline, and then if I kept staring at the outline I would see the large, misshapen, gossamer, see through energy of the aura. Sometimes I would see colour in this energy.

During this period, I discovered Jeff had been seeing a woman in Spain. She was the reason he'd had a change of heart. Connor was friendly with this woman's daughter, and encouraged a friendship between the two parents, as he didn't want his dad being on his own. This was ironic, as I was the one who encouraged Jeff to invite Connor to accompany us on the adventure. When I broke off our relationship, Jeff returned to Cardiff within two weeks, leaving Connor in Spain. I had quite a few of his belongings in my home, and he called to collect them. We sat together for an hour and it was obvious Jeff wanted reconciliation as, once again, he was hinting. He said, 'I'm going to leave the UK as I've nothing to stay for'. When I didn't comment he said 'If I had something or someone to stay for, then I would stay'. I just acted sympathetic, but non-committal. The conversation continued in this vein for quite a while. Eventually Jeff said he had to go.

When he left I cried. I still had deep feelings for him, but wanted no more pain, no more bad choices, and, of course, I had the guidance from HQ. I had no excuse for getting things wrong; I had to listen to this guidance. I felt respect for myself and knew I deserved better than what was on offer. At last, I had learnt my lessons well. When I went to bed that night I spoke to HQ and asked him why I was so attracted to people who caused me pain. I had a dream that gave me the answer. In my dream I was walking along, and my head and upper torso were inside a piece of a jigsaw puzzle. The edges of the jigsaw were protruding from my body. Coming towards me was Billy, my ex-husband. He was also wearing a piece of a jigsaw, and as we went to pass one and other our jigsaws locked together – they fitted. We had a bit of a struggle to unlock ourselves, and eventually we walked away from each other.

I continued walking and coming towards me was Michel, my ex-partner. He was also wearing a jigsaw and, as with Billy, our jigsaws locked together as we went to pass each other. There was another struggle as we tried to unlock ourselves. Other people were passing me and they were wearing jigsaws, but I was OK with them, as our jigsaws didn't match. I noticed the jigsaws had a gossamer quality about them, just like the aura. When I woke up, I half-understood what HQ had shown me.

A couple of days later I had a call from a lady called Janice. Her husband Geoff had been one of the healers at the clinic. I had spoken to Janice on the telephone on several occasions but we had never met. She asked if she and her husband Geoff could visit, she had something she wanted to tell me. I was happy for them to come, although I was mystified as to the reason.

114

When they arrived I made tea, and the three of us exchanged pleasantries. Janice told me she wanted me to be the first person to know that she had divorced Geoff a few years before, but she had kept this a secret and was still living with Geoff as man and wife. She said Geoff had brought her years of emotional heartache, and she told me about their past, which included Geoff's episodes of adultery. Janice said she didn't want to be known by his surname anymore. She was reverting back to her previous surname, and she said what that surname was. When she said the name the effect was like an electric shock running through me. Neither Janice nor Geoff knew that this slightly unusual surname was my Jeff's surname. I couldn't say anything, as their visit was not about me it was about them, and most importantly, Janice. I thought this was a real coincidence, but I knew there was no such thing as a coincidence. It was another stunning example of synchronicity. Geoff jokingly said he would change his surname to her new surname as he still loved Janice. He said 'I will be known as Geoff -----'. I understood the message HQ was giving me, and was so glad I had made the right decision regarding Jeff. At last I was being sensible, no more weakness. I was proud of myself.

In early December 1996, the estate agent rang and made an appointment for people to view the house. Just before their arrival I ran up the stairs, and a photograph of the house that hung in the landing had moved. It was completely off centre. I said to HQ 'I'm moving, aren't I?' The people loved the house and, as they were a cash buyer, asked if I could be out by Christmas. I had twenty days to pack and leave. A couple of nights later I went to bed and, although it was bitterly cold, I started to feel excessively hot.

Eventually I got out of bed and opened the curtains and windows, to let in the cold air. In the sky were bright, coloured lights. They looked like search lights, and they were over my house. I almost had the impression it was some kind

115

of aircraft or spacecraft above me, but only the lights were visible. I would say there were around twenty beams in all. I leaned out of the window to get a better look. The house was on a bend, and coming from the right I saw a silver car, possibly an old Mercedes. There was what I thought looked like a woman with long blond hair driving. She was staring intently at my house and I thought 'She's going to crash if she doesn't look at the road'. The car seemed to glide around the bend, and disappeared out of sight.

Within moments the car was coming back, but this time from the left. I realised what I'd thought was long blond hair was in fact a white hood, and on closer inspection the face seemed sexless, neither male nor female. Again this person didn't look at the road, but was focused on my house. The car drove out of my vision and, within moments, was coming back from the right again. I watched this person stare at my house, with the car gliding around the bend and the face turning as the car turned, so the house never left their vision. When the car disappeared I waited expectantly for it to reappear, but it didn't. I looked up at the lights, and they were gone. I felt freezing cold. I knew I had been influenced to witness these things, but what did it mean?

I tried to work it out. Joyce had taught me symbolically a car is a person, and a Mercedes would be regarded as one of the best; it was an old car, so could that mean an old soul? Silver is the highest form of spirituality. Was a highly spiritual person being sent to me? I never did get an explanation of what this meant, and I am writing this story in 2005, some nine years after the event. Perhaps I never will know, although I like to think it was representative of the spiritual power that was focused on me.

The next day I told Kim and Chris about what happened in the night. I was amazed when Chris said he had seen the lights, and thought they may have been over my house. My home was elevated, while theirs was on lower ground, but we lived near to one another. I was so glad I had a witness to part of the experience.

With the house sold, I felt I had to take advantage of my unique situation. This was the first time I was totally on my own, with no person, animals, or home to look after. I had missed out on the adventure promised by Jeff, and so wanted an adventure of my own. I spoke to Kris and he encouraged me to go for it. He said 'Get out there mum and have some fun'. Kris had met a lovely girl called Jane, and they were talking about living together, and so I knew he wasn't on his own, and this was a comfort to me. I rang my cousin Linda in Middleburg, Florida, and she invited me to visit her. I stored my belongings with family and friends, and stayed with my parents for Christmas and the New Year.

In January 1997 my neighbour Hilary and her husband Colwyn drove me to Birmingham airport, and waved me goodbye. I had a one-way ticket, and in my head spoke to HQ and said, 'I promise I will return when you tell me'. Linda and her grandchildren met me at the airport, and we hugged and screamed with excitement. All Linda's family were waiting for me at their ranch home and Don, her husband, had prepared a celebration meal.

Don and Linda were the most generous and loving hosts. Their three grown-up children and their families were equally fantastic. Don's father Walter lived in his own annexe attached to the ranch, and he was very entertaining. A car was put at my disposal, and I had freedom to explore and go wherever I liked.

For the first four weeks of my being there Linda worked, but she gave up her job to spend time with me. I loved their easy way of life. There was so much space everywhere. The ranch house and grounds were really big, and they had horses, and Linda and her children were expert horse people. They had a natural limestone swimming pool and I would swim, or lay on the edge of the pool reading a book.

My Aunty May and Uncle Fred, who were Linda's parents, were both dead. Linda took me to the cemetery where they were buried. It was a cold and drizzly day, and as we sat on the bench opposite their graves, the sun came out. It was a really spiritual moment. We sat and talked about our families, the afterlife and our beliefs. Nana Beatty was Linda's nana as well as mine, and our mothers were sisters. I told Linda of the communication I had received from Beatty since her death. Linda was fascinated, and I discovered she was quite spiritual herself. We talked of spiritual things on many, many occasions after that and I started to teach Linda the things I'd learnt.

Linda's brother Chuck was a policeman in Salem, Massachusetts, and he wanted to meet me, and so he and his friend Paul flew to Florida for a two-week holiday. They arrived at the Ranch in a convertible car, with the hood down, looking very American, and they immediately tricked me. Paul pretended he was Chuck, and Chuck pretended he was Paul. I was so confused, and that set the tone for the holiday; they were such fun to be with.

Linda and Don owned a lakeside house, as well as the ranch. We all had a fantastic time at the lake. Don would cook on the barbeque, and we would sit around with drinks. I lost count of the number of times I was thrown in the water, and Linda's son Ryan used to take us out on his speedboat. He would pull a large inflatable tyre behind the boat, with one or the other of us sitting inside the tyre.

At the lake house there was a granny annexe. Linda and I had redecorated it with a Native American theme, and there was quite a spiritual feel to it. Chuck and Paul slept in the annexe, and Linda and I would visit them, and would sit around talking about spiritual things. The two men were completely fascinated by my stories, and Chuck would nag me to take them on guided meditations.

It was obvious Chuck would make a good spiritual medium, as he received communication the first time he linked to the spirit world. I would teach them about the universal language of symbols, and interpret their dreams for them. We didn't just sit around chatting, but went out and about as well. We went to Daytona Beach, St Augustine, and Gaiter Land. A highlight of the visit was going to Jacksonville to see the famous country singer Garth Brooks in concert. That concert was amazing. Garth Brooks came on stage in a glass spaceship, which rose up from the ground. We sang along to his songs, and we loved it.

Most days Linda and I were chauffeured around in the convertible, with the roof down. We ate at fabulous restaurants, usually sampling the locally caught fish, and drank margaritas with crushed ice. The weather was stunning. The night before Chuck and Paul were to leave for home, a crowd of us went for a night out. We went to a country and western bar and had a wild time; Paul had to be driven home in a pick-up truck, as he was the worse for wear. He had discovered he could never drink Don under the table.

The next day Paul was really ill during the flight home. When they arrived back in Salem, Chuck rang me. I had been telling Chuck about the power of the mind, and how you could telepathically communicate with others by thought. Sitting on the plane before take off, Chuck was in his seat at the back of the aircraft. A woman was walking in the aisle, quite a distance from Chuck. She was obviously looking for a seat. There were quite a few available, and Chuck decided to project thoughts to the lady, directing her to choose a particular seat. She made her way down the aisle and sat on the seat next to Chuck, which was where he had wanted her to sit. He thought it was hysterical, and couldn't stop laughing. He was really pleased. In the years following our meeting, Chuck went on to develop his spiritual gift, and I am proud to say he is now a highly regarded, practicing Medium living in Middleburg, Florida, near to Linda.

I was so sad when Chuck and Paul left. Linda and I missed being whisked off here, there and everywhere. After being in Middleburg for seven weeks, I had the thought in my mind to ring an airline in Orlando and I inquired about a ticket back to the UK. I told them I was looking for a bargain, and it didn't matter when I travelled. I left my name and contact number with them, and they said they would get back to me. I spoke to HQ and told him, 'It's over to you, if you want me to go home, you can influence the airline'.

Weeks went by, and I had the most fantastic time with Linda and her gang. I drove everywhere in the car they lent me, and I had a wonderful sense of freedom I'd never experienced before. Linda was in no hurry for me to go anywhere. She and I were firm friends, and we never stopped laughing together. On 12 April the airline rang and said they had a flight to the UK, leaving on 14 April and I could fly with them for $35. My mother's birthday was 14 April, and when I looked at my passport, it was the last date I could legally stay in America. The fact I was on a ninety day visa had completely slipped my mind. It obviously hadn't slipped the notice of HQ.

I left my American family with fantastic memories, a grateful heart, and an uncertain future. How the plan would unfold, and what lie ahead, was a mystery to me.

I flew into Gatwick Airport, and there waiting for me was my dad. He had come to escort me home. That gesture really touched me. I was looking forward to seeing my son and the

120

rest of the family. When we arrived at my parent's home my mum, Kris, Gail and Tracy were waiting for me. It was wonderful to see them, and I realised how much I had missed them.

I was homeless, but was able to stay with my mum and dad. I didn't know what to do, which direction to take, and kept asking HQ for guidance. After about two weeks I decided to walk around Cardiff Bay, to see what changes had been made to the area. I stopped to have coffee at the Cardiff Bay Hotel, which was on Schooner Way, and as I looked out the window I noticed a For Sale sign on a flat opposite. I had time to kill, and so rang the agent to ask if I could view the property. The Agent said his colleague was conducting a viewing at the flat in thirty minutes' time, and he arranged for me to view before that appointment. I finished my coffee and went across the road.

I was shown around the flat, and immediately fell in love with it. It had wonderful views over the East Dock, and I knew my Norwegian grandfather had often sailed in to that dock. Everything was very light and airy. The lounge had patio doors to the front and side, and there were two large bedrooms, as well as a good-sized kitchen and bathroom. I found myself saying I would buy it, and I didn't even haggle with the asking price, which was quite unlike me.

I went home and told my parents what I'd done, and my dad was quite worried. I had £36,000 and no job, and the flat cost £60,000. At the time you could have bought a three bedroomed house for that money. I started to worry as well, and was giving myself a hard time for being so impulsive. However, once confirmation of the sale arrived from the Agent, I changed my mind. I couldn't believe what I was seeing; the block the flat was in was called Beatty Court. I truly didn't know this when I viewed the flat. As far as I was concerned the address was Schooner Way. How could I doubt this flat was for me after such a wonderful and symbolic connection? The synchronicity was stunning.

The agent told me the people viewing after me also wanted the flat, and they too were willing to pay the asking price. I had pushed in on their appointment, but I couldn't feel guilty now that I knew this was meant to be. The next problem I faced was getting a mortgage. I spoke to my nana Beatty and HQ and said 'OK, if I am meant to buy this flat, you will have to help me get a mortgage, and to do that I need a job'. So far the agent hadn't asked too much about my financial status, as I had given them the impression money was no problem. I gave them the names of my solicitor and hoped for the best, leaving it to HQ to sort.

I didn't have a clue what to do about work, and as I had been self-employed for so long, I wondered if I was unemployable. I decided to join a temping agency and put my shorthand and typing skills to use. The agency sent me to an executive search and selection recruitment company in Cathedral Road, just at the edge of the city centre. The Managing Consultant was a lady called Jan, and she needed a Personal Assistant. Jan and I hit it off immediately. She was very efficient at her job, and taught me to use the recruitment software, as well as explaining the search and selection process. I loved it.

I was busy handling the response to advertisements, and making appointments for Jan to interview the candidates she had selected. I was also doing the research for, and making the initial contact with, head-hunted candidates. The company handled senior-level appointments, but never mind how high powered the candidate, they had the same worries and fears as any one else. I would spend time with the candidates talking and reassuring them, and injecting them with positivity and confidence. I was like a mother hen looking after her brood, and I was in my element. Jan was really happy to hear of my marketing skills, as she needed to

Nana Emily, me and nana Beatty on my wedding day in 1971.

My mum and her friend Peggy, they were neighbours in Llanrumney and stayed
lifelong friends.

Uncle Emrys, Aunty Maureen, mum and dad in their younger days.

My mum with four of Maureen and Emrys's grand-daughters.

ady with scroll in her
and in my former home

The flats where I lived in Beatty Court, on the East Dock.

Kris fishing at Roath Park Lake in Cardiff

Chuck, his wife Stefanie, and Linda in America. My cousins' mother was the eldest of my mother's four sisters. Her name was May and she married Fred who was an American GI

My sister Gail and me.

My niece Tracy

Her beautiful daughter Sophia, the light of my life.

Kris with our dog Lola, whose camera shy.

Me and my dad

Me Kim and Chris, eating as usual.

Kim and Chris with our dogs Silky and Lucky

Sophia at two years of age

grow the business, and after four weeks she offered me a full time position, which I gladly accepted.

Our Office was part of a national recruitment organisation, and we had to follow the recruitment process set out in the company manual. All offices acted completely uniform, so that all employees were interchangeable from one office to the next. My role expanded when I became an Auditor for the company. Periodically I would visit other offices to carry out an audit inspection of their working practices, to ensure they were complying with the system.

During this time I had heard nothing from the estate agent. I rang around mortgage companies, but was told I would have to be employed by my new company for six weeks before I could apply for a mortgage. I was worrying about the flat but couldn't ring the agent, as I didn't want to be pushed to exchange contracts. Unbelievably I still hadn't heard from the agent when the six weeks continuous employment was up, but after I applied for the mortgage I felt able to ring them. I rang and said I was worried, as I hadn't heard from them for such a long time. They apologised, and I was told they were loath to ring me as the owner of the flat had put a tenant in for a short stay, and the tenant still had two weeks to go, having signed a two-month tenancy. I felt like laughing, but decided not to confide my situation to them, and I was very aware, once again, HQ was orchestrating events.

I eventually moved in to the flat on 1 July 1997. However I didn't move in on my own. My sister's daughter Tracy had bought a house with her boyfriend, and she had recently found out he was cheating on her. She was upset, but was determined not to stay with him, and she asked if she could move in with me. I was happy to have her with me, and was grateful she was sensible as, even though her boyfriend said he was sorry and wanted her back, she was firm in her decision, and eventually he bought her out of their property.

Within the first week of our living at the flat my mum brought her one surviving sister, Joan, to visit. Joan had married Jim and lived in Shropshire. Jim had died quite a few years before. He had been a real animal lover, and it was he I asked to meet my pets when they past over.

We were sat in the lounge drinking tea, and I had the patio windows on tilt. A rose somehow came through the tiled window and landed on the floor between us. We couldn't believe it. We were in a third floor flat, and it seemed an impossible feat for this to have happened. My Aunt said 'That's from Beatty,' and I knew it was true, I could sense Beatty around us. I went to bed that night and had a dream. My nana Beatty was stood at my front door. In the road was a beautiful limousine with the passenger door open. Beatty pointed at the car and said to me 'I have to go away for a while', and she hugged me. I watched her walk away and climb in to the car, the door closed and she was gone.

Tracy stayed with me for a year, and we lived together very amicably. During that year I had rejoined Joyce's education class, and within a short while Joyce hired a hall for the classes and I began teaching the beginners. A lovely lady called Ann would teach the intermediate level and from Ann the students would pass to either John or Joyce. We were very busy and the classes were extremely successful. I usually had about ten people in my class, and I loved working with the students and seeing their development. People would also telephone me or call at the flat for help and spiritual guidance, and very often I would give them a reading.

I was also working one night a week as a volunteer at an Aids Helpline, and I stayed with them for a year. I learnt a lot from working there, and met some really lovely people. The HIV virus is a dreadful thing, and has a devastating affect not just on the carrier, but on their family and friends. One of the worse aspects of this virus is the stigma that's associated with it. That same stigma was attached to leprosy, and is born of ignorance and fear. This was one of the aims of the helpline, to educate the public about this virus.

At the helpline I met a lovely young man called Keith, and he shared his story with me. He had been diagnosed with HIV at the age of twenty. He had just finished university and had applied for the job of his dreams. Keith had worked hard for this moment and was really excited, and quietly confident of success. The company requested he have a medical, and an appointment was made with the company doctor. Keith went for the medical and was not at all worried, after all he felt really healthy. His world was shattered when his job application was rejected, as the medical had shown he was an HIV carrier.

Keith told me he was gay, and from about the age of eleven he had struggled with his sexuality. He said he hadn't asked to be gay, but he was gay, and he'd had to face that fact. He lived in a very small and close knit community and he feared exposure, as he felt this would bring condemnation. When he left for university he hadn't 'come out'. He wanted the chance to live openly as a gay man and find confidence within himself before he faced his family. He had his first sexual encounter when he arrived at University. He was with this male partner for about a year. Since that relationship, Keith had two other sexual partners. He emphasised he wasn't promiscuous, but did admit that occasionally he hadn't practiced safe sex.

Keith was a good story teller, and I felt his pain. He said his mother had been waiting on the end of the telephone, anxious to hear the good news about the job. The whole village were also waiting for news, and now there was to be no job. Keith felt he had joined the ranks of the 'living dead' and would be shunned by society. This was how he saw it. His family were so proud of him, and he was the first family member to achieve a degree. Of course, they didn't know he was gay and were totally unprepared for the bombshell that would explode around them. Life had dealt Keith a cruel blow. He said having to tell his family and friends was the worst trauma ever. He felt dirty and ashamed.

Keith was twenty-three when he told me his story, and his family had long since come to terms with his life. He said they continued to love him, and were as supportive as ever. He was re-building his life and felt able to look forward to the future. I thought Keith was a remarkable young man and I was privileged to have met him.

I really believed at last I was getting to grips with life. My son Kris was still with his girlfriend Jane and they decided to buy a house together in the north of Cardiff. I was really happy for them and when I saw their house I was thrilled. It was so nice. Tracy was getting sorted as well. After living with me for about eight months she formed a new relationship, and eventually she and her new partner decided to buy a house together. They began looking around and settled on a house in Caerphilly, just outside Cardiff. The legal process for the purchase was started, and Tracy began packing to leave. She had been with me for a year.

My sister Gail had previously been married to Tracy's father for seventeen years, but the marriage had long since come to an end, and Gail had met someone else. His name was Frank, and Gail had been with him for eleven years. At the same time as Tracy was planning for her new life with a new partner, Gail's life with Frank was coming to an end. Tracy moved out and within weeks my sister Gail and her twelve-years-old rottweiler dog had moved in. My sister needed a lot of looking after, as the split with her partner hadn't been amicable. When they met my sister owned her own house, and Frank moved in with her. Initially he never earned a lot of money, and only ever paid her a token sum for his keep. She was a positive influence on Frank, and with her guidance he was eventually able to get a good job, and his earnings increased substantially.

After living together for about nine years Frank persuaded my sister to sell her house, and invest in a new home with him. Although they put equal amounts into this new property, my sister spent extra money decorating and furnishing it.   She loved her new home and was very proud of it, but within a short period of time Frank began acting differently towards her. It seemed he got carried away with his new status, and was talking of buying expensive cars, and generally acting as though he was wealthy.

While my sister was busy homemaking, he was busy out and about. His behaviour was so different; she asked him if he was seeing another woman. He protested his innocence and caused a fuss, saying he couldn't believe she didn't trust him. She was so down about her situation she took time off work, and was walking through the centre of Cardiff one day. Coming towards her was Frank, and he had his arms around a woman. The three of them came together and Frank held his arm up, palm facing towards my sister's face, while drawing the woman closer to him in a protective gesture, and said 'It's not what you think Gail', and they walked past my sister. She was left standing, feeling upset and humiliated.

That was the end of their relationship. After a lot of shouting and persuading on my sister's part, Frank went to stay with his mother, and my sister began packing her things. It was decided Frank would pay her a sum of money, and then the house would be his. My sister felt, quite rightly, a great injustice had been done to her, and she beat herself up for her lack of wisdom. She wanted to get away from him as soon as possible, and she asked if she could stay with me.

I seemed to lurch from one situation to another. Life was full of surprises. I would start planning for something, and would find my plans being derailed, as life would throw something else at me. I viewed these happenings as 'meant to be', reasoning I was now so sorted I could handle everything. With hindsight I realise things were thrown at me so that my free will could take me as far as I needed to go to learn lessons, and I still had a lot to learn.

With my sister severely depressed, any plans I had were put on the back burner. I would go to work, come home and sit and talk with her, trying to make her positive about life. I talked about the amazing coincidence of her seeing Frank with the woman in town, and tried to convince her there was a plan for her life, and like me she had to learn lessons before she found the right path.

Although my sister was a healer and a spiritual person, the hurt had gone very deep and she seemed to lose her faith. She stayed with me for about a year, and when she moved out I was really depleted. I was so desperate for her to be happy that I had given her all my energy. I had the highest motives for helping my sister, but she told me I had made her feel very inadequate, and she felt I was judging her, and this really shocked me. Our parting was not a happy occasion. I now realise that like me, my sister also suffered from low-self-esteem. It brought home to me how frail we humans are.

Looking back I can see I was wrong. The more my sister had withdrawn in to herself, the more I had taken control of her situation. I was weakening her, as well as weakening myself. HQ had ensured I learnt a vital lesson, and one which would have the most impact on me because it involved my sister.

Just before she moved out, and before I realised the effect I was having on my sister, I had a dream. In my dream I was showing a lady around my house. The lady seemed familiar to me and I was trying to please her. My house had beautiful rooms. Everything was spick and span, and the furniture was highly polished. I would show her around one room at a time, but she seemed very disapproving. I kept the best to last, and showed her in to my bedroom. There were patio windows in this room, and I opened them. Stepping on to the balcony there was an amazing view of a great expanse of sea. I looked to this lady, expecting to see approval on her face but instead, was distressed to see she was shaking her head.

As a result of my spiritual education I was able to work out my dream. The house was me, and I had done a lot of work on myself, getting myself cleaned up and polished. Windows are our view on life, and as they were opened patio windows, this showed my view had opened up. The sea is the sea of life. My view of life was now immense. The guidance in my dream was showing me I had opened myself up to this person but they weren't happy with me or my view on life.

Obviously my sister's opinion of me had an effect on our small family. My parents felt my spiritual beliefs were the cause of the problems between me and my sister. There was some truth in what they said, as I did keep reinforcing to my sister her pain was for a reason, and kept trying to get her to see the bigger picture. I was probably the equivalent of a religious zealot, and with hindsight I should have backed off and let her hurt, and then heal in her own way.

In August 1999, a few months after my sister moved out, her daughter Tracy gave birth to Sophia. This beautiful child was a gift to our family. Even if we weren't in harmony about some things, this precious child brought us together on another level. Sophia looks so much like Tracy and she has the most sunny and loving personality. My sister Gail loved being a grandmother and my parents were thrilled to be great-grandparents.   I was certainly thrilled to be a great-aunt.

However, my mother was very critical of my spiritual work, and made negative comments every opportunity she got. All through my trials and tribulations I had managed to stay positive, I had always managed to survive. Now I started to feel different. Life lost its shine. I think this was because when I came back from America I honestly thought my life was going to be wonderful from then on. I arrogantly thought I had been through the pain, and now would come the gain. There was a change taking place in me that I couldn't control. I couldn't take criticism in any way. I was defensive and felt extremely self-pitying.

I would go to my education classes and teach, but whereas before I wanted to help everyone and save the world, I started to feel withdrawn and detached. I told Joyce I couldn't continue teaching, and was relieved to walk away.   I had a circle of friends who lived around me, and these friends were colourful characters. They were the town set, and led very glamorous lives. I would go out with them on occasions, and loved to watch everyone interacting. They were wonderful to me, always including me in their plans but now I started to feel I couldn't be around them. The world seemed to be an unkind, frightening place, Beatty had deserted me and HQ was silent.

Even my work was now a problem, as Jan had left. The company brought in a replacement for Jan but things didn't work out and so the office was closed. I started a new job as a recruitment consultant instead of my previous role of support, but I hadn't appreciated what a competitive environment I was to work in. I seemed to be a misfit. I found fault with everyone, and those around me seemed to have really bad character flaws. It was as if my senses were heightened and any little fault was magnified. I found the whole culture hard to deal with and after nine months looked for another job.

Again I joined a recruitment company as a consultant but discovered that the two managers were really horrendous. They were a proper double act and I felt they were bullying, sarcastic and cruel in their treatment of the staff, and they fostered an environment of unhealthy competition. They talked behind everyone's back and ridiculed peoples lifestyles. I was becoming more and more sensitive to people, and this sort of behaviour was making me feel ill. I was staying in on my own in the evenings. My smoking accelerated, and on the weekends I started to drink alcohol in the flat, and I would sit thinking. I had never done that sort of thing before.

When Kris or the rest of my family would telephone or visit, I would switch to animated mode, and I believe I was a good actress. If it was the weekend and I had a drink, I wouldn't answer the telephone, and would say I had been out enjoying myself. I was sure no one knew what was happening to me, as no one ever said anything. My thoughts were becoming more and more morose and self-pitying, and I began to think of death. I would think if I slid in to the freezing waters of the East Dock under cover of darkness, and I swam to the middle, I would drown. My death would be recorded as accidental, and my wonderful son and family wouldn't know what I'd done. These were only fleeting thoughts, and I know I would never have carried them out, but it was a scenario I enjoyed playing over in my mind.

I couldn't believe my new life in my lovely flat had gone so wrong. I couldn't be around people without them having an adverse effect on me and so what was the point. It had taken two years for me to slowly slide to this level of despair, and I began to frighten myself. I pleaded with HQ, 'If you are there, please help me', but I didn't know if he heard me.

I visited the doctor and told her what was happening to me. I also confided that I was experiencing a strange noise in my ears. It was like an electric, static type of noise. Sometimes there would be a slight hum to it She said I was showing signs of stress, and needed time off work. She was happy to write me a sick note and offered to give me tablets, but I refused any medication. My doctor also wrote for an appointment to have my hearing checked, although when I went to the appointment, they couldn't find anything wrong.

Days later Kris visited me. He said he and Jane were going through a bad patch and had decided to sell the house. They both worked very hard at their jobs, and thought it was sensible to move out of the house while it was up for sale. That way it would be tidy for the viewings. He wanted to know if he could move in with me. I was really sad to know he and Jane had problems, as she was a really lovely girl, but I told Kris he could move in when ever he wanted.

Kris is such a positive personality, and has always been so independent. When he moved in, he brought life in to the flat, and always came home in a good mood. He would order us takeaways, have his music blaring, and his friends would be back and forth. My son is a bit of a comic, and he constantly made me laugh. Under his influence, I began to feel better and I stopped smoking and drinking. Kris and Jane's house sold quickly and although they were friends, he and Jane decided they would go their separate ways.

Over the next few months Kris had a really good time. He loved the fact the flat was on the edge of town. He could walk to the pubs and clubs within twelve minutes and, as he is a fisherman, he could sit on the East Dock fishing, and pop up to the flat for cups of tea and food.

After about eight months, as there was only one bathroom and we now had lots of extra visitors to the flat, I said to Kris perhaps I should buy a bigger place. Kris said he thought we should buy a large three-storey house together, and we could have separate facilities. I was shocked at this and said 'Surely you want to buy a house of your own?' He replied, 'I don't think you are ready to be left on your own yet mum'. I looked at my son, and wanted to ask why he thought that, but I couldn't bring myself to say the words. His words implied he knew I had been struggling. How had he known? I was positive I'd kept my distress to myself. My son has grown up with my spiritual beliefs, and I know he is easily influenced by those in spirit. I believe this was an example of that influence. I said to HQ, if I am supposed to move, then I know you will influence events, and I will listen to you.

I never went back to my job, as I didn't feel up to facing such a competitive and negative environment, and I intended to stay on the sick for a while. I wanted time to go back over my life and face myself. I already knew I was prone to feeling sorry for people, and this made me want to carry them. What I didn't understand was how, even though I knew my weakness, I still kept following the same pattern. I also needed to understand why I no longer fitted in with so many people. It seemed that my energy no longer blended with theirs, and it was like a physical hurt.

I knew I did over and above what was expected of me in order to help people. When I had a need, if I didn't get this same level of support back, my low-self-esteem would kick in and I reacted badly. I was weakening others, as well as myself. My whole life seemed to have been one disaster and I felt sorry for HQ, having to work with me. I was constantly asking him to show me where I was going wrong. I realised he had backed off for a while, as I obviously needed to suffer in order to grow, but just recently I had started to feel him around me again.

Five

Making the move

Now I understood about spirit communication and my faith was absolute. I had to learn some final lessons which would lead me to take a leap of faith into the unknown, and begin my work as a professional spiritual medium.

Kris designs software for a living. I asked him if he would design a web site for me, as I thought I would share some of my knowledge with the world. I would be able to interact with people from a safe distance. He built a fabulous site for me and I was spending lots of time answering emails, interpreting dreams and generally chatting to like-minded people. This kept me busy and I was enjoying my new found occupation. I began to think I should start to work professionally as a medium, and the more I thought about it, the more compelling the idea became. I decided to set up a limited company and advertise my services and I set about organising this.

I had a friend who I'd known since working at my first recruitment company with my colleague Jan. He had recently started a recruitment company of his own in Bristol. He had never been involved in recruitment, and so this was a brave step for him to take. My friend was constantly asking my advice, and picking my brains. When I went on the sick he saw this as an opportunity for me to share my knowledge with him, and kept asking me to work in his office. I declined on quite a few occasions, but he was desperate. Apparently for the period of time he had run the business he took very little income. He had other means of financial support, and so wasn't destitute, but he couldn't continue to work in the business without seeing some growth.

Although I resisted working with him, I did agree to care-take the office while he had a holiday. I was able to see at first hand the systems used for the recruitment process, and it was chaotic to say the least. It was going to be a mammoth task introducing a working system to the office, but as I knew exactly what was needed I felt a spark of interest, and within a couple of weeks had made the decision to join him. I came off the sick and went back to work.

The first few weeks in the job were a whirl of activity. I had to give my friend and his two assistants IT lessons. I also had to explain the recruitment process, and the systems needed to turn the office into a functional recruitment company. He needed my expertise, but working with him and getting him to embrace a workable method was hard slog. I realised I had changed so much that any discord was becoming intolerable to me. My friend needed what I had to offer, but my capabilities damaged his ego, and he was unable to acknowledge the difference I made to the business.

HQ sent me a dream. I was walking down a path and glancing to the side, saw a steep hill. There were people spread out on the hill, and they were having difficulty climbing. I could see them reeling around, bumping in to one and other, and losing their footing. I left the path and ran part way up the hill, and to the nearest person to help them climb. It was such hard work as they were not making an effort to help me help them. I was calling others to join us, and with my arms extended was pushing the people forward. We got to the top of the hill and I collapsed. The people I had helped ran off, laughing and chasing one and other. I wanted to join them but had no strength left, and they didn't wait for me.

When I awoke, I understood the guidance I was receiving from HQ. Thanks to him and the dream I could see what was happening. Every time someone needed help, I would jump in without thinking of the consequences, and this behaviour was costing me dear. I was constantly coming off my path. I was so easily distracted and wasn't focusing on my own development. Looking back, I should have acknowledged I had made a mistake in joining my friend's business. I should have been brave and walked away. However, I am a true cancerian and never know when to let go.

In the office the feeling of irritation was strong with me, and I had to struggle to control it. I wanted out, but couldn't find the courage to leave a job half done. Occasionally I would get a call from someone wanting my spiritual services, and I would book them in for a reading or spiritual guidance. I loved those occasions, and put a lot of energies into marketing my new spiritual venture in my spare time.

Meanwhile, Kris and I were looking for a house to buy in the Bay area. We viewed a really large, three-storey property, very near to the flat. It was more money than we could pay, and the agent told us the owners had already turned down an offer of less money, and so it was no good us trying to negotiate on price. Reluctantly we dismissed this property and found another three-storey but smaller house. This was in our price range, and we liked it, but not as much as the other house. We made an offer on the smaller property, and it was accepted.

I had put the flat up for sale and immediately got a buyer. We were so excited, and our mortgage and moving arrangements were all put in place. We were exchanging contracts, and completing the sale and purchase on the same day. I wrote letters informing everyone of our change of address, but as the date got nearer I started to feel dread. Suddenly I was having strong emotions about the house we had chosen. I couldn't visualise us living there, and the feeling got stronger and stronger. I tried to speak with Kris about it, but he was very set on buying the house, and dismissed my fears. The day the legal work was to be completed came. I woke in the early hours of that morning and couldn't get back to sleep. I lay feeling so disturbed and unhappy about what we were about to do. Kris went to work, but was due back about twelve to help with the move. Everything was packed and ready. By nine I had worked myself into a terrible state. I knew I couldn't go through with it. It was completely the wrong thing for us to do.

I had made so many mistakes in my life; I couldn't ignore my inner voice. I rang the solicitor and told her I had changed my mind and she was to cancel the purchase of this new property, and hold the sale on my flat. I had to cancel removals and send letters to various people telling them we would be at the flat address for a while longer. I rang my buyer to tell them there was a delay. They were buying the flat as an investment, so they weren't too put out about this.

I rang Kris with dread, and had to tell him what I had done. He went mad. He told me I was neurotic and was seeing problems where there were none. He was angry that I had made the decision without consulting him, but all I could tell him was I knew there was a reason for what I had done, we were just not seeing it yet. The lady we were buying from went ballistic when she knew. I felt really ashamed about it, but I was confident there was a higher power involved in my decision, and I knew enough to know I couldn't go against it. I cried on and off all day, as I had so much hostility directed at me, and I kept asking HQ for confirmation that I had been influenced to take this course of action. I kept thinking 'What if I'm wrong?'

Later that day a lady called Diana rang me. She was a new friend. I had met her a few months before at a mutual friend's house. Diana had asked the friend for my number, as she said she felt drawn to me. She had called on a couple of occasions previously, and when she rang that day I felt a bit peeved, as I was obviously not in the mood for making small talk. Diana told me she had been in my area that day. She was re-arranging a friend's furniture, as they had their house up for sale, and it wasn't selling. She said 'Perhaps you know it; it's the big house off Schooner Way?' I immediately became interested and said 'But didn't they refuse an offer on the house?' 'Yes, that's right' she said, 'and they regret not accepting it'. I then told Diana what had happened that day.

I rang Kris and told him of this fantastic coincidence, and he said 'Mum, this is the reason we weren't meant to buy that other house'. He had forgotten all his anger towards me, and completely accepted the situation now that he could see a purpose to what had happened. I quietly said a big thanks to HQ.

We bought the big house and we moved on 1July, 2002, and I remembered this was the date I had moved in to the flat, but five years before. The day we moved we acquired a cat, as Tracy had moved house and her cat Mr T was not happy with his new surroundings. He was brought to us to see if he would settle, and he's been with us ever since.

My birthday is on 9 July and my sister's birthday is on 11 July. She and I were rebuilding our friendship, and we decided to fly to Dublin, Ireland to celebrate. While there I felt the need to visit a medium, and found one working very near to where we were staying   I sat with her and she said to me, 'I am being told you should be reading for me', and I laughed. She asked if I had just moved, and I told her I had. She said 'This is a large house, and you will be working at the front of the house. People will come from all over to see you.' She also said 'Spirit are telling me to tell you they led you to this house, and it was quite a twisty, bumpy road, but the timing had to be right. They are saying to tell you the house has good energy'. She then went on to say I would work all over the world and she said 'When you come to Dublin to work, please look me up'. She told me lots of other things, and she also gave me evidence of Beatty's survival. I was blown away by the reading and knew I had a lot to think about.

Gail and I had a really good time in Dublin, and we both made an effort to build fences. She had long since got over the trauma of the break up of her relationship. When the holiday came to an end I had my new house to look forward to. I hadn't even unpacked properly, and so I had a lot to do.

I wasn't looking forward to going back to work after my short break, and immediately I went in to the office I felt depressed. It is so difficult to implement changes in a way that won't offend those whose systems you are changing. I would find myself presenting the changes in a placating way, as if I didn't my friend and his assistants would display signs of indignation, and would take offence. I had to give them lots of praise, and it was really tiring. This was so ridiculous, as the reason he wanted me there was to bring in these changes.

I asked HQ for help and a couple of days later I had a dream. I dreamt I was in a riding stables and a man allocated a horse for me to ride. I went to the horse and before I could mount him he spoke to me. He said, 'I don't feel very well. Different people are mounting me and taking the reins. They ride me and pull me to the left, and the right, to the left, and the right,' and he demonstrated this by jerking his head from side to side.

I was devastated for this poor horse and immediately went to the man. I said to him 'My poor horse is ill. Different people are riding him and treating him roughly. They are pulling him from left to right, left to right. This must stop.' The man said 'You will have to buy him from me.' The man named a price, but it seemed much too high a price for me to pay. I argued with him for a long time, and as this was happening someone ran to me. They said 'Your horse is dying.' I was in a panic and ran to my horse, but he was lying on the floor. When he saw me approach he lifted his front leg for me to be close to him. I lay down beside him with his leg over the top of me, just as though it were an arm. We were cuddled up to one and other.

I said to him, 'Please don't die. I am sorry I took such a long time arguing with the man about the price, but I'm going to buy you. No-one else will ride you ever again.' The poor horse said 'It's too late, I'm dying.' And I was screaming 'No don't die, please don't leave me. I will pay the price; I promise I will pay the price.'

I woke myself up as I was crying out loud. That dream had such an impact on me, and it was very easy to interpret. A horse is a power – horse power – and I was constantly handing my power to other people. They were pulling me all different ways, and were treating me roughly, and I was letting them. I was too weak to pay the price of taking control of myself. I was being told my power could not sustain this. This had been the theme all through my life. I knew it and yet I still acted the same way. With each new situation I had an argument going on in my head, and yet I still gave way to my repeated pattern of behaviour. I said to HQ 'Please don't let it be too late, I promise I will be different, never mind what the cost and who I offend, I will be different. I am going to take control and put all my energy into achieving something for me.'

With great relief I told my friend I was leaving, and a veneer of friendship was placed over my last few days in the office but the day I left I was so relieved to be away from him. That night when I snuggled down in bed, when I closed my eyes I could see a big eye on my eyelids, and it was open wide. I knew what I was seeing was my third eye, and it was amazing to think I had seen it all through my various stages of development. Finally I now knew my worth, and knew I was going to put all my efforts in to promoting my own spiritual business. The thought of working with HQ, and reaping the rewards for my own hard toil was liberating. Never again would I feel sorry for anyone if it was inappropriate to do so. If I made a mistake, I would acknowledge it and let go of the situation, I wouldn't hang on regardless. I had learned so many lessons and knew from now on I would help people, but I would never carry.

I would stop letting other people influence me and I would listen to that inner voice. Looking back, I realised this was what it was all about; I had found the vital ingredients needed to change my life. It had taken me a long, long time to get there and reading back on my words I groan at my stupidity but I can't re-write history and I have to accept that this is how it is and was.

Six

Back to the past

So here I was armed with all my knowledge, and it was as though I was going back to the past, but this time I had been given the opportunity to do it right.

Before starting on my spiritual work I was invited to accompany Gail and her two friends Karl and Ingo on a five day longboat holiday on canals in the West Midlands. This was such a treat, and Karl very generously paid for the boat. I can honestly say this was a fantastic way to relax, and we had such fun. We cruised by day and ate and drank at night. Karl's family lived around the area, and they joined us at various stages of the holiday. When I arrived back home I felt ready to take on the world.

The house was still full of unpacked boxes. There was so much room I was spoilt for choice as to where things would go. Kris was quite sorted on his floor at the top of the house. I live on the middle floor and we share the ground floor and, just as the Dublin medium told me, I work at the front of the house. At the moment my arrangement with Kris works perfectly, although Kris has told me he'll be looking for a place of his own soon. He obviously realises I feel so much better. He's bought a speed boat, and he spends hours on the water in the Bay. He runs his own IT company, and is dabbling a bit with property. He seems to have got life right and is such a balanced person. How he got to be that way I haven't a clue, but I realise my son has taught me a lot. He has helped me immensely, but he has never carried me.

We are a very happy household, and we've acquired a dog to keep Mr T the cat happy. Lola came from the local dog's home, and she and I spend hours together. As I am working from home a lot, she is great company. It is like going back to the past when Lucky and Blue were with us, and just as they did, Mr T and Lola keep us laughing with their antics.

We have a cat flap in the kitchen, and when we first had Lola she would follow the cat through the flap. As she grew this became more and more difficult, and yet she would squeeze herself through this small space until, in the end, she had to admit defeat. In the evenings Mr T loves to walk with Lola and me in the local park, and this was something my other animals did. Tracy's daughter Sophia stays with us regularly and she is a real joy, she is such a positive, loving and sunny child and I adore spending time with her.

It was wonderful to be free. I knew I could support myself financially for at least two years as I had money put away. Now I could concentrate on driving my spiritual work forward. I did myself a business plan, and gave myself a marketing budget of £2,000 per year. I was very specific in my advertising. I was not a fortune teller and didn't want anyone asking for a reading about their future. I wanted to give evidence of survival to people who were bereaved, to offer spiritual guidance to those who were in trauma, and also to teach spiritual education and development, and help others connect to, and work with, the universal power.

I devised an advertisement which got this message across, and my telephone numbers and web site address were always displayed prominently. I began receiving emails and telephone calls from a variety of people. Some were looking for tarot readings, and I would explain I worked with my mind, and didn't need a prop. Even though my advertisement was quite explicit, people would still ring asking for fortune telling, and I would turn them away. It would have been so easy to see these people just to bring in some money, but I was determined to stay true to my beliefs.

Sometimes people would phone in a distressed state. I would spend long periods of time talking to them and, of course, this didn't earn me any money. I had emails from people asking questions and looking for answers to problems. I would spend time answering these people, and again this didn't earn money. However I was very conscious of helping people without carrying them.

People started to come for readings, and some of their stories were so traumatic. After the reading I would sit chatting to them, listening to their problems and as I had my spiritual education, I could answer their questions. I never worked to a set time frame, and gave the client as long as they needed. I was determined everyone would leave me feeling better about their situation. I couldn't take away their grief, but I could give them comfort and hope.

My work as a professional, spiritual medium was taking off and the mix of people and problems that were coming my way challenged my skills. My background was now of tremendous benefit to me, as nothing I was told fazed me. I had heard and seen it all before, and I realised I had wisdom. The price I'd paid to acquire my life experiences suddenly seemed worth the pain. HQ repeatedly told me, 'No pain, no gain'. I have now extended my range of services to include counselling and life style coaching as, although people might initially come to me for a reading, I soon realised what most are actually seeking is guidance. I really love that part of my work and I am proud to say I truly do make a difference to people.

Nearly every time I speak to someone who has contacted me regarding my work, I ask them the same question. 'Do you receive spirit communication?' They invariably answer 'No.' I then ask them a series of questions and very often they answer 'Yes' to at least two of them. They are amazed when I tell them they are in fact receiving communication and guidance from the spirit world. The questions I ask include:

Have you seen colour or images on your eyelids when you close your eyes?

Do you think of someone and then see or hear from them shortly afterwards?

When the phone rings, do you know who is calling?

Do you experience coincidences?

Have you had dreams that you retain when you wake?

Do you ever sense and/or smell anyone around you?

Have you ever wondered where certain thoughts come from?

What about objects moving, and/or electrical interference?

Have you found yourself coming out of your body, or perhaps you remember being out of your body?

Do you have premonitions or an inner knowing?

Have you experienced sleep paralysis?

Do you see movement out of the corner of your eyes?

The more people I questioned, the more I began to realise that nearly everyone was receiving some form of spirit communication, but because they had never been told what to look for, they didn't recognise it. I thought back to the times I had looked for answers other than the spiritual theme. I had wondered whether I was psychotic, or whether because of my mother's problems, we had inherited a genetic mental imbalance. I even used to think about my short periods when I experimented with drugs, although I recognised I had communication long before my drug days.

It is liberating to know there is an army of people like me out there. I tell these people with confidence I believe they are receiving spirit communication, and once they recognise it, they are usually hungry to learn more, and some of them join my classes.

Of course, my conviction isn't just based on the random happenings I have experienced, but I am able to look at everything that has happened to me as a whole. I have the benefit of being able to work as a medium, and HQ has been with me every step of the way. I feel sorry for him having such an imperfect subject to work with. It has taken me more than half my life to listen.

I know without a doubt that we all survive bodily death. We come to earth in the physical body to learn lessons and gain wisdom, in order to progress spiritually. Our natural state is in the world of spirit, but in that world we don't have the human frailties like hate, greed, and jealousy. Nobody progresses through experiencing just love, and that is why we are living a life on earth. We need to experience adversity, and this life on earth can be your hell. We come here with free will, and we have guidance and influence from those in the spirit world, to help us achieve what we came here for but, of course, we don't have to listen.

Talking with people gave me an insight into belief systems. Most of us are born into a religion and when we are young we accept what we are taught with blind faith, I know I certainly did. Any spiritual experiences we have along the way we attribute to our religion, and it entrenches us further into our particular belief system. For instance, in times of great adversity a Protestant might see Jesus, or a Catholic might see Mary. I believe these visions are representative of the spiritual power with that person, comforting them in their time of need. They are shown this power in a way they can accept. Sometimes we will fight to the death for what we have been taught.

I believe in God and I now know he is a power that is universal, and that power is within every single one of us regardless of our beliefs. I know Jesus and other religious figures did exist, but I believe they were human just like you and me, and when they finished their mission here on earth, they went back to their natural home in the world of spirit. These figures were chosen by God to come to earth and live a life in the physical body to teach us something, and lead by example. These chosen people must have been very highly evolved spiritually, which is why they were chosen. They would have agreed to the plan for their life, and understood the reasoning behind it. Their spirit, with the mind locked, would have been placed in the womb at conception, when the sperm and egg met.

When they were born they would have had no idea that they had come to earth to carry out a special mission. However, the spirit workers working with them would have guided and influenced them, just like they guide and influence us. The difference would have been that, because these figures were so highly evolved, they would have listened from the beginning.

HQ has taught me we live many, many lives and it is not just earth that is used. There are other planets in the universe that are used for our progression, and with each new life we learn a little bit more. These chosen people must have experienced many different lives, and probably on quite a few different planets. This is how they earned and developed their immense soul growth.

I now realise the religions we subscribe to are man made, and they have changed over time, to keep pace with a changing society. A lot of religious text has a foundation of truth, but over the years these texts have been open to interpretation and, of course, a lot of what is written is symbolic. However, we have lost the way to interpret the universal language of symbols, but with this new Age of Aquarius this language will now be revived.

If only the whole world could think in a more spiritual and unified way, then perhaps it would put an end to wars. We are all here for a purpose, and each of us has a plan. We all come from the same source, and will all go back to the same place.

Each time we live a life on earth we gain experience and grow in wisdom. In each new life the mind is locked, and so what we've learnt before isn't accessible to us. However, the soul isn't locked, and this is responsible for our empathy and compassion, and contributes towards making us the unique person we each are. For instance, if someone had previously lived a life in a body that was dreadfully disfigured in some way, when they were re-born in another life-time they might feel a great empathy and compassion towards people with disfigurement. They wouldn't know why they felt this way, but they just would.

Our natural home is back in the spirit world. This is where our spirit family are, and the spirit family isn't necessarily the family we are born into when on earth. When we die we go to the astral plane and have healing and our mind unlocked. The full extent of who we are and what we had come to earth to achieve would be known to us, and we then judge ourselves.

The astral plane is another progression level, just like earth. We can stay there to continue our progression and work in service to those on earth. If we leave family behind when we die, we can also come back and forth to them, to let them know we have survived, and try to influence their lives. The bonds of love never die.

We stay on the astral plane for around one hundred years, the same as we do on earth. This is where your spirit workers, such as guardian angels and guides, are working from. The person who works with you from conception and throughout your life I call the guardian angel. The specialists who come to help with particular parts of your life, I call guides.

Imagine if you had been a brilliant brain surgeon when living in the physical body. You could continue to share your gift with those on earth whilst living on the astral plane. You could be a guide and channel your healing power through healers, or you could influence other surgeons. If you were an accomplished musician, once you died and went over to the astral plane, you could influence other musicians, helping them achieve their true potential.

The power of the unlocked mind is incredible and it is this power that can interfere with electrics, influence coincidences and so on, all with the intention of getting us to start wondering about these things. Hopefully, we then start to search for knowledge and in this way we expand our minds and gain wisdom.

If you were a dreadful person when living on earth you would not be allowed to work from the astral plane. When you died you would go there for healing and the mind would be unlocked and the extent of your sins would be known to you. Once returned to your true state, to see where your free will had led you would be such a sorrow to you.

It would be like someone on earth, who was normally a good person, getting drunk and causing death by drink driving. When they sobered up and realised what they had done, they would be inconsolable and in deep grief. This is how it would be if you were a wicked person when on earth, once your mind was unlocked. You would have to go back to your spirit realm, where your family are, and you would put yourself in purgatory. It would take a long, long while for you to forgive yourself and then eventually earn the forgiveness of others.

A spirit family stays together throughout eternity and can only move up the realms when the whole family is ready, and has reached a certain level of understanding. In this way each one of us has a reason to continue our progression, as we have a lot of people relying on us. We stay on our realm for a period of time and then back into the physical body for up to a hundred years or so, and then on to the astral plane for another hundred years or so, and then back to the realms, and on it goes. This means we are in a continuous cycle of progression.

Of course, sometimes a cycle can be interrupted. It could be there is a particular reason for you to get to the astral plane from your realm. If there was a job of work for you to do on that level then you would need to touch earth first. Imagine an aeroplane landing, it needs a certain amount of runway to enable it to slow down and land.

The rate of vibration on the realms is very high, the astral plane vibration is lower and earth is lower still. To get to the astral plane from the realms we need to touch earth first. This could be through abortion or miscarriage. I do not mean to suggest we should attribute all these happenings to a spirit plan, but sometimes these things are part of a plan. However, no-one is ever lost. If any of us dies before our time or before we had a chance to draw breath, on to the astral plane we go, and our life continues.

Remembering HQ had died in the 1920's, this would mean he had been on the astral plane for about thirty years before I was born. I asked him how he had spent those years and he said 'My world is like your world. There is constant interaction with those who live around me, and I have been able to continue my education by visiting our wonderful places of learning. My main task during those years was to help my family still living on earth'.

I thought this was fascinating, and then asked 'How did you come to work with me?' HQ said 'About two years before you were born on earth, a plan for your existence was put in place. Both you and I agreed to that plan and had plenty of time to prepare for what was to come.' I asked 'Does this mean I will die when I am about seventy? You will have been on the astral plane for about one hundred years when I reach that age.' And I was told 'Your time of death is recorded, you can go before, perhaps because of an accident or illness, but you can't stay after and I can only tell you, you have a lot of work left to do. The cycle of years I have given you is approximate. Sometimes people have stayed much longer on the astral than the average one hundred years. It all depends on the job they are doing.'

I had to admit HQ had a way with words and everything he told me was always very logical to me, but I do not want to give the impression I can talk with him just as I would someone living on earth. Our communication can be quite frustrating and includes thoughts, sensing, dreams, symbols and visualisation. It takes a lot of effort to understand the communication.

People constantly ask me 'If we still live after we have died, why can't we come back and speak clearly instead of all this cryptic stuff?' I always laugh when I hear this and say 'I wish!' but the answer to that is we come here on earth to learn lessons. If we knew everything there was to know, and if spirit communication came loud and clear to everyone, then we wouldn't have to make an effort to learn. We wouldn't stretch ourselves. We are given carrots by those who work with us from the spirit world. They try to lead us forward, to get us to be where we are supposed to be. In order for us to grow we have to expand our minds, and think out of the box. We need to be open to the wonder and possibility that's all around us.

Symbolism is a fantastic means of expanding our minds. Imagine if the whole of the population of the UK couldn't read or write. To relay information to anyone, other than speaking with them direct, we would have to draw picture images. These picture images would be symbolic of what we were trying to say. It wouldn't matter what language we spoke, the pictures would tell the same story. For instance, an arrow used as a road sign is pointing us in the right direction. Everyone can understand that, and the arrow is a symbol.

Much of our understanding about the universe and its history is turned on its head when we are confronted with the on-going discoveries of cave drawings and such like. In certain parts of the world primitive drawings of animals, spacemen and spacecraft have been found. These images speak to us in a symbolic way and present a puzzle, which challenges our grasp of reality.

Science is now recognising the survival of consciousness after death of the physical body. It is also recognising that consciousness, or the spirit, is separate from the physical body. We know that the brain is a mass of physical cells in which a lot of electrical activity takes place. The human brain is both a transmitter and receiver, just like the television. However, you can block the signals of a television by putting it inside a shielded chamber and the television wont work. Experiments show that if you put a medium inside the same shielded chamber it does not prevent the medium from receiving specific and verifiable information.

Experiments are ongoing but the research of some very well respected scientists indicates that the human brain is a receiver and a transmitter of energy and information from outside our physical bodies. The brain is merely a tool through which consciousness or the universal mind works.

Quantum physics has opened up our view of the universe. HQ tells me this will lead to mankind having the proof and understanding that we are all spirit living a life in a physical body to learn lessons and progress spiritually, and that we all survive bodily death. Once we have complete understanding of the atom it will blow apart our present belief systems and, hopefully, the whole world will progress to a more unified and tolerant way of living.

I love teaching and helping people develop spiritually, and I have found a really good venue in a local hotel, where they provide a classroom setting, complete with a flip chart and overhead projector. We can dim the lights and make the room really atmospheric for when we do visualisation, and it works well for all of us. However, I am hoping to buy a building in Cardiff that can be a centre for spiritual education and development, healing and spiritual counselling. It would be wonderful to have this facility where people who were hurting, grieving or seeking knowledge could go.

My classes are twelve weeks long, one lesson a week for three hours a lesson. That's all that's needed for most people. During the twelve weeks my students have many, many spiritual experiences, as the spirit helpers working with them are anxious to show they exist. I stress to the students what they are learning is not blind faith. They have to have their own experiences in order to understand and accept.

I hold a maintenance class every six weeks for students who want to continue developing in a group environment, sharing their experiences. I also host two functions a year, where all the students old and new can get together and have a good time. Other than that, they're all out in the big wide world doing their bit.

I tell all my students, just because they are receiving spiritual education, it doesn't mean they will work as a medium, but they can be their own medium. However, it does mean they can be in service to the universe. The spirit workers can use them to help those in need, and I caution them to help but never carry. I also tell them to keep their feet on the ground and leave the 'me' out of it, and never be boastful. That way, their egos won't get in the way of the work. They must listen to the inner voice and take notice of the universal language that's all around them. They have to let their spirit workers guide and influence them, to help them to be where they are supposed to be.

Seven

Working with spirit

My work, continuing to learn, and the students' stories.

I have met so many wonderful people through my spiritual work, and I thought it would be nice to let some of my students tell their own stories. These next few pages are devoted to them.

DYLAN'S STORY

My name is Dylan and I am thirty-one-years old. From a child I have always loved to read about ghosts and frightening things, but as I grew I became more sophisticated in my understanding of spiritual matters. What I needed in hindsight was spiritual education, because until you get it your susceptible to every Hollywood idea and scary story going about the spirit world.

I first became a pupil of Yve's following a very successful reading I received from her in April 2004. I had thought about attending a spiritualist church but as a person who has never considered himself religious the idea of praising and singing has always put me off. The first thing I noticed when I attended the classes was how different we were as pupils. There were teachers, housewives, civil servants, students and care workers, all from different backgrounds but all drawn once a week to a function room in Cardiff bay. All of us had shared spiritual experiences to some degree, and it is this fact that first made me realise how generally wonderful this phenomenon is.

Since I was young I have been a comedian, and loved to make others laugh but never had I considered making a career out of my talent. In our first lesson we were taught to link to the person who was working with us from the spirit world. I was surprised to find out that my guide had been quite the comedian himself in his day, when he lived on earth. He represented himself as an Italian jester.   I could clearly see his face in my mind and it was as though I was meeting

158

someone who I felt I'd known all my life. I now realise it was his influence that was bringing out the comedian in me.

As the weeks progressed I was inspired to try my luck at a local open mike night for stand up comics, and I had to work out a routine. I remember being perplexed as to why all my ideas for the comedy routines seemed to come to me in the kitchen. I would be washing a cup by the sink and an idea would suddenly form in my mind. I would get the sponges and the scourers out and before I knew it I had a well developed idea, and a sparkly kitchen. Yvonne explained that certain rooms in the house hold different symbolic meanings and functions. The kitchen is a preparatory environment where things are put together, so that's where you will find me when I am creating routines these days. Since my first stand up attempt I have been gigging quite regularly. I always ask my jester for guidance and influence just before I step on the stage. I feel his presence with me, and it is amazingly comforting.

Just recently I was made redundant and was looking for a day job to support my newly found comedy career. I ended up working in the office of a local taxi firm on the telephones. That first day I got chatting to a young lady called Samantha who was working next to me, and was astounded to find we had a few things in common, including a love of comedy. Samantha and I were blown away when we realised the first stand up routine I did, she was in the audience and she herself was a budding comedian working in the same venues as me. And here I was sat next to her on the first day of my new job. How's that for a coincidence?

Prior to this one of my class mates called Nathan had given me a reading in which he saw the image of a sewing machine. I had no idea what this could have meant at the time but I was amazed to discover Samantha is a gifted seamstress who actually owns her own sewing machine. We are now together as an item and we get on really well, and can still barely believe how we met.

The classes have long since finished, but once you step on to the spiritual path you realise you can never go back to how you were, and you look at the world around you in such a different way. We are constantly learning and growing and the classes give you the capability to understand the lessons along your path.

EDWARD'S STORY

My name is Edward and I am a thirty-four-year old skilled tradesman. I am a very sensitive person, a proper people pleaser. I am from a working-class background and was brought up in the South Wales Valleys. I have always known there was something more to this world, even as a child my imagination worked overtime. I was really interested in life after death. Growing up in the valleys within a small mining community taught me about life, and even though I knew about hardship and such like, it didn't stop me making bad choices that led me into trouble, and caused hardships of my own.

Recently my bad decisions and my compulsion to please brought me real heartache. My partner of six years broke off our relationship and I couldn't cope with my emotions. During the six years I was with her, I had organised my life around her and put her before family and friends. She was my world, and I sought to please her constantly, and she was happy to take what ever was on offer.

I was ceremoniously dumped just before Christmas 2004 and, as a result of this, took time off work. I visited a psychic operating out of a shop in Cardiff. He gave me fifteen minutes of his time at the most, took my money, and told me I would meet somebody with blonde hair and blue eyes and I

160

would have to choose between two women. He also told me my girlfriend would never come back to me; we would be friends or lovers but would never have the same relationship again. He said I would get married just once, and would outlive my partner. I was really unhappy with what he said and it wasn't what I was looking for. It didn't help me at all.

I was in a very vulnerable state, having suicidal thoughts. In desperation I picked up the local business directory. A lady's name jumped out at me. Her advertisement said she helped people with trauma, and I was certainly traumatised. The lady was Yvonne and she agreed to see me immediately. I was with her for two hours, and for her time I was charged a fixed fee, and came away with a tape of our session. This was a bit different to my previous experience and far better value for money.

My father, who had died five years before, made contact. He gave me evidence that it was him connecting, and also gave me guidance about my life, where I had gone wrong and what I was to do to rectify it. It all made perfect sense. My dad had been my best friend, and the whole family were still grieving for him. To know he knew about my life, and was able to help me even though he had died was amazing. He emphasised I was to widen my social circle.

After the reading Yve explained to me about the mind, and how we think so we pulsate. This pulsation or frequency was attracting people to me who were happy to take, and I was able to play out my role of pleasing. It made perfect sense. She told me my father had said he would give me evidence he was around me, and she explained the various forms of spirit communication. She also said I needed to make mental changes, to alter my pulsation.

That night I was in my bedroom and a cupboard door opened wide. I knew this door was closed firmly. I had a sensing that told me this was a spiritual happening. When I thought about it, I realised this cupboard had swung open before, but I'd ignored it. A week later a picture hanging on my bedroom wall started to move back and forth. I looked at this, and wanted to ensure nothing was causing it to happen. I checked windows and doors for a draught, all the while the picture was moving. In my mind I said 'Dad is that you?' and the movement became stronger. Around the same time my television was acting up. Tele-text would change pages on its own. Also I was getting amazing coincidences. I would think of someone and the phone would ring and there they'd be.

One night I woke up from sleep and I was paralysed. This had happened to me before, and was frightening. I couldn't open my eyes or mouth and it was as though I was pinned to the bed. When I eventually came out of it, I phoned Yve. She told me I had woken too soon; my spirit wasn't properly in my body. My spirit was either going to, or coming back from the astral plane, where I would benefit from the wonderful guidance spirit helpers could give. She said the body was like a car, and without the driver it couldn't move. The spirit was the driver. I understood perfectly what she meant.

I started to have psychedelic colours on my eyelids, and sometimes I would have a sensing someone was with me, out of the corner of my eye I might see a shape or a light, but if I turned to check this out, it would vanish. Yve told me I was seeing with the peripheral vision of the third eye. Therefore, if I tried to look with the physical eye, what I had seen would be gone. I was thrilled with all these fascinating experiences and because Yve was so good at explaining them to me, I wasn't afraid.

I began to see faces on my eyelids, and one face was very prominent. It was a man around my age; he was very good

162

looking and seemed full of character. Slowly I began to feel differently. It was really comforting to have my dad back, and my upset at the failed relationship started to recede. I was starting to realise my past experiences were valuable, as they make me the person I am. I have learnt it is not good to be a people pleaser. Sometimes the people you are pleasing don't deserve your attention, and I know I deserve to receive, not just give.

Remembering my dad had told me to widen my social circle, recently I moved from my Valleys town to Cardiff Bay. I have made new friends, and they mix well with my old friends. I go out and about to the pubs and clubs in the Bay, and enjoy life. I have a six-year-old daughter from a previous relationship and I spend more time with her.

Recently I joined Yve's spiritual education and development class, and I am starting to understand about life. I am continuing to have amazing experiences and the prominent face I had seen on my eyelids is back and forth to me constantly. I have discovered his name is Michael, and he is my spirit worker. I realise I have a gift, and I want to use this gift not only to help myself, but to help others.

GILL'S STORY

My name is Gill; I am a forty-five-year old woman and have two lovely teenage daughters. I work full-time as a Mental Health Social Worker. I have always believed in the afterlife and always felt things around me. I have had life experiences that have made me think 'How could that have happened?' or, 'That was meant to be'.

Last year my marriage was breaking down, well it had been for years but was coming to the point I needed to make a decision. I was very unsteady and lacking in courage and confidence. I had many readings with mediums over the

163

years, and I suddenly had the urge to want to learn more about things that weren't tangible.

One day in work I was chatting to one of my colleagues around this subject and he said 'I have been training with a woman in Cardiff who teaches spiritual education'. Wow, I was so excited and almost immediately rang Yve, I remember saying to Yve, 'I can't explain it, but I want to know things and do something different.' Yve knew exactly what I was feeling and trying to say. I decided to join her classes and, although still in pain, I felt supported. I realized it may take time, but I knew I was going to be okay. This all seemed to be developing at the 'right time'.

Classes begun, but I was all over the place, preoccupied with my pain, but nonetheless gaining strength from the teaching. I benefited greatly from Yve's support and guidance during numerous calls I made to her in sheer desperation. On numerous visits to Yve's home, she explained to me what was happening, the vibrations and the aura, our dysfunctions and how we attract dysfunctional others, and how we can change this pattern of behaviour.

Here I see a parallel with my work, dealing with depression and its devastating effect. In my work we talk about raising self-esteem and self-confidence in dealing with life events. We discuss positive thinking, and avoiding negative people, to surround ourselves with people and things that bring us positivity. It would be interesting and useful to offer spiritual teachings, as Yve's classes offer a far greater understanding of how we work and why negative thoughts have such a devastating effect.

It is now six months since I discovered my husband was having an affair, even though the marriage needed to end and we were destroying each other, I was devastated. Again I would ring Yve when he continued to rub my nose in it with

164

his cruel behaviour. Yve would calmly explain the situation and demonstrate how I was being supported and guided.

I realised my husband was no good for me, and needed to be out of my life for me to be able to grow, as he hadn't grown and was holding me back. Whatever job I have come on earth to do, I would never have been able to achieve if I remained with him. I certainly wouldn't have reached my full potential, whatever that may be.

I did the whole course with Yve but because of my traumatized state I felt I hadn't fully appreciated the experience. I have rejoined the classes, starting at the beginning again, but now I am absorbing and fully participating. I have had some electrical interference. The coincidences, well they have been stunning and have given me opportunities to find a way out of my problems. I also have a tremendous 'sense' of being protected and guided and I know that all will be okay. The difficulties I am experiencing at the moment I know are happening for my highest good. I now listen to my 'gut feelings' and I will not make a decision or commit myself to anything if I am slightly unsure. I give the person working with me from the world of spirit the opportunity to influence me, and when that happens then I act. It is so much better to be proactive rather than reactive.

From a professional perspective, we are now encouraged to offer a holistic assessment of the patient including emotional, physical, psychological and spiritual needs. This looks more at the person as a whole. It is interesting to note the spiritual needs, as there is now an acknowledgement of this. Although there is argument that someone talking of spirit may be deemed by mental health workers as a mental illness.

Religion or spirituality I guess has always been a contentious subject, and maybe in the past patients would avoid sharing and discussing their beliefs with workers for fear of being seen as either having a mental health problem, or the potential to develop a problem. But a belief or faith can mean a massive arm of support to be aware of, and may go a long way in explaining or making sense of a person and their situation. From what I am learning in class with Yve, a lot does run parallel with our work in mental health now, but I would like to see more involvement of someone highly spiritual like Yve, to share her knowledge, maybe with students of both the medical and social school.

This would go some way in preparing before qualifying. There is room for psychiatry and sometimes things do go wrong for people, but not all, and it should not be an automatic assumption that a person is mentally unwell just because they hear voices or listen to guidance.

Learning more as I am in Yve's classes, there is massive scope to challenge the psychiatric system, but I am not knowledgeable or confident enough yet to do this on a large scale, but certainly on a smaller scale.

This has to be a beginning........

JASON'S STORY

My name is Jason and I was first introduced to Yvonne in November 2003. The events leading up to our meeting were quite bizarre. I had hurt my back in October 2003 and was bed bound, by early November I was seeing lights and shadows passing in my bedroom, at first I put these down to imagination – I had after all been in bed for a month. However as I started to take more notice of them they intrigued me. I have always believed in an afterlife, and always felt there was a part of me that I was yet to discover.

I had my first spiritual encounter when I was ten, and I will never forget it. It was 2 February 1987 to be accurate, and

166

the evening before I had written a letter to my great grandmother. She was in hospital and I wrote that I missed her and hoped she would be home soon. During the early hours of the 2nd I woke up in bed and sat upright. At the bottom of my bed was my great grandmother. She was talking to me but I couldn't hear her, she smiled and left. I went back to sleep with the knowledge that my great grandmother was obviously out of hospital and better. I was so happy. When I woke up in the morning I discovered my grandmother had passed away in the early hours.

I grew up with my mother, sister and brothers on a council estate in Wales. My mother always relied on me as the eldest to make sure that the rest of the kids were up, dressed, fed and ready for school. I used to also make her a cup of coffee and take it to her bedroom at eight every morning. Years went by and this was the normality of my day to day life. I was constantly relied upon to do the daily tasks of the house.

In 1990, I had a big falling out with my mother and I went to live with my grandparents. I couldn't take the pressures of having to be the "Man" of the house at the age of thirteen. I always yearned for a childhood, but I feel that was not meant to be – It wasn't in the plan. I didn't speak to my mother for two years. We would pass like strangers in the street and this was hurtful. Eventually I went to see her. We made up and slowly started rebuilding our relationship; however it was never the same. She was almost like a big sister or close friend.

I went away to university and learned about life, and I met someone and fell in love. After graduating I bought my house in 2001. My partner and I decided to live together, and I was really happy and so proud of myself and my achievements. Meanwhile I had heard from my sister that things weren't good at my mother's house. She had rent arrears and unpaid bills everywhere.

167

In April 2002 I had a call from my mother saying she was in the railway station in our home town. She told me her house had been taken off her and she was coming down to Cardiff. She arrived at 10pm that evening. She brought with her two dogs attached to ropes, two cats in a box, a rabbit in a box and my young brother dragging a big laundry bag of possessions. I knew in my heart of hearts that this episode in all our lives was going to be disastrous and that things would never be the same – yet again.

My heart sank for her, but she didn't seem to care, in fact I would say she was excited. I drove them all back to the house and then went to the supermarket and spent over £150 on food and extra supplies for the house to accommodate them. I also had to buy leads for the dogs, cat litter trays and a rabbit hutch. She lived with us until July 2002 by which point we could take no more. My once new home had become the playground for a bunch of untrained animals. The house smelt and no wonder, as the dogs would go to the toilet everywhere, and my mother would sit in her chair and try and justify what they were doing.

My partner and I had tried absolutely everything to help her. I got my brother a place in school, and I had council housing application forms sent to her. We genuinely wanted to help her, but she didn't seem to want to help herself. She wanted to be looked after, and gave no thought to me or my partner and the effect it had on our lives.

The house became unlivable and my partner and I lived in our bedroom, and when I say lived I really mean lived. We would come in after work and literally go into our room and banish ourselves from the rest of the house. All our friends were banned from visiting and we found ourselves getting deeper into debt in order to keep all of us. All talking and actions failed with my mother. I was left in a very painful place, and what followed would mean to this day I haven't seen her.

My mother, brother and I went back to our home town on 12 July in order to prepare for my sisters wedding on the 13th. I hadn't made any plans for what followed next, but I knew things could not go on as they had. I got to my grandparents and spoke with my grandfather. He was very supportive of me and said that I had done the best I could but I should not go on this way. I was relieved to hear him say this. It gave me the courage to telephone the local housing authority. I told them that as of the Monday my mother would be homeless. I cried for hours and couldn't believe what I was planning. It all seemed so unreal, so pre-conceived and contrived.

I said nothing on the Saturday, and everyone enjoyed the wedding. I remember dancing with my aunt and mother and my aunt was saying to my mother she wanted her back. She told my mother she missed her company. I thought 'wow, this must be a message of sorts, and I am doing the right thing'. I realise I was looking for any signs to appease my conscience.

On the morning of the 14th I went to pick up my mother to take her to my aunts house for a visit. She got in the car and by this time I had decided I would have to leave her there and return to Cardiff without her. I distinctly remember driving on the back roads to get my mum to her sister's house, and I will never forget the emotions that were going through me. I ended up crying so hard at the wheel of the car that I lost all feeling in both my hands, my mother was really concerned and asked what was wrong and I remember making up a really sad excuse. I left my mother at my aunt's house. That was the last time I saw my mother and that was in July 2002.

I drove home to Cardiff, and a journey that normally takes three and a half hours took six hours. I was crying all the *way, and the only way of explaining the feelings were that of a person who was grieving, and if truth be known it was grief, I was grieving for the relationship that had died. I was also feeling guilt because I never explained to my mother or anyone else what I was doing. I took the easy way out.*

The following months I was a mess. I couldn't think straight and felt real self loathing. I finally reached an all time low and I ended up in counselling. The counselling helped me understand what had happened, but I still could not get over it. By October 2003, things were improving slightly. I was back in touch with my mother by phone only and we had started to talk about the events. She still blamed me for making her homeless and not helping her, and I still despised the fact that she had completely ruined my life. Even by telephone she was getting me down.

In October a friend and I went to have a game of squash. I tried a new warm down routine which debilitated me for the next couple of months. I was completely bed bound and had plenty of time to reflect on the events of the past twelve months. My partner was so good to me, and friends would come round and help but I was still very depressed and I felt lonely.

After a couple of weeks I started seeing the shadows, I thought nothing of them at first but then they became more evident. I started seeing circles of colour and flashes of light from nowhere. I decided to visit a medium to have a reading. There was something prompting me to do this and as soon as I became more mobile I went through the yellow pages and found a number for Yvonne Bailey – Spiritual Medium.

I rang her immediately with anticipation. She was busy at the time, finishing another reading with a lady called Paula. We made the appointment for the following day, which was Saturday. It was a real problem trying to maneuver myself out of the house and into the car but I just knew I had to do this, and I went down to Yve's for our appointment.

I knocked the door and this cheerful face greeted me, this was Yvonne. She was a far cry from previous mediums I had visited. No dark cloths and burning incense. She made the whole thing very normal. Yvonne proved existence after death to me by giving me evidence from my grandfather and my aunt. I was there for nearly two hours chatting away, and she told me about spirit communication and the basics of symbolism, and what happens when we leave the physical body. I was very excited, so when she told me that she ran a class I jumped at the chance of learning. Little did I know that I would be developing alongside Paula, the lady who had been having a reading the day I had called to make my appointment.

Our lessons went on fantastically and each time we visited it became much more interesting and simple. The colours, the symbols, the electricity surges were all forms of communication. Going to my lessons really comforted me; it also gave me confidence to deal with people on a different level. I realised I had lived most of my life to please other people. I had to know my worth and work hard at changing my repeated pattern of behaviour.

The whole process continues to this day. I have grown so much I hardly recognise myself. I am still getting lots of communication from my spirit workers. They let me know they are around as my TV switches itself on and off, my lights dim, and there are cold spots in my home. The coincidences are never ending and I get amazing guidance through my dreams. I work hard at interpreting the symbols.

I am always very wiling to help others but I no longer carry and constantly try to please. It is great being in service to spirit as I can guide others when they are in need, and if I cannot help, then I know a very close friend who can!

JULIA'S STORY

From a young age I have searched for answers to life, I felt there had to be more to life than what I had been taught at home, in church and in school. The feeling was an inner knowing but hard to describe.

As I grew older I began to develop my spiritual side and would read everything I could on the subject. Many of my friends were also spiritually inclined, and so I used to regularly have 'psychic parties' where we would invite a medium to come to my house and everyone would have a reading done individually. We were always astonished at the accurate information we obtained, and hence kept on the lookout for anyone with a good reputation whom we could visit.

This is how I first came across Yvonne, browsing through a business directory; I saw her advert, and felt drawn towards her. I made the call, and Yve explained she specialised in bereavement and trauma rather than general group readings. She had also told me about her classes and she answered questions for me. I had felt a great connection towards her on the phone; little did I know what a huge impact this woman would have on my life!

A few months later, I was still thinking of her and the things she had told me. I looked up her website and read all about the development classes, which spurred me to contact her again. After talking with her I decided to join her classes.

I was desperately searching for something as my life was in bits. I had recently reported historical sexual abuse to the police. I was in the middle of a turbulent time with

172

statements, and court proceedings. I also had to come to terms with the hostile reactions of my family. Hence I decided to go and seek knowledge, to continue my search about the meaning of life, to help me through this life.

These classes gave me the biggest insight that I could ever have hoped to gain, I learnt that all of the 'coincidences' I could never explain in my life now had some meaning. All the recurring dreams that had baffled me finally made sense, and I learnt how my own thought processes were leading me into a damaged way of living. I was repeating the cycle of abuse by living as a victim. Yvonne's classes taught me that because I was focusing on my past, I had a negative energy, and was attracting people with a similar negative energy which fitted my own. This was obstructing me from moving on with my life. I had previously got involved in 'damaged' relationships, dated an alcoholic, and made friends who had turned out to have ulterior motives.

Incredibly I was lucky enough to have married a fabulous man with a positive attitude, who persevered with my negativity and has helped me realise my potential. I am positive he was sent to me by my spirit workers. I learnt how to communicate with spirit, and through Yvonne's guidance met my own guardian angel called Shane, who has now become a huge part of my life!

Once the classes started, we were encouraged to maintain notes of any spiritual activity that took place. Suddenly so many signs were being shown to me and I knew I was not alone, and that I was being looked after. Shane would make the TV flicker every time I entered the room, light bulbs were suddenly blowing all at once for no apparent reason, and children's musical toys would sound even though they were not touched! I started to realise that Shane had been working with me all my life, but it was only now I was recognising the signs. I learnt the spirit contains a mind and a soul. The mind is for thought and thinking and lies over the heart area; the soul is for feelings and emotions and lies over the abdomen. When we wake from sleep a sort of periscope rises from the mind to the brain and it has an eye. The eye sits in the forehead area and is referred to as our third eye or sixth sense. Yvonne explained the physical body is like the hardware of the computer, our mind is like the hard-drive (where all the information is stored) and the third eye is like the mouse of the computer, and it interacts with the brain, relaying instructions to activate the body.

A few months earlier, I had been summoned to attend Jury service, and at the last minute my venue was changed from Swansea to Cardiff Crown Court. Coincidentally I was allocated to a case identical to my own, where a woman was also reporting historical childhood sexual abuse.

I now sincerely believe that I was taken to that court and case for a reason. It gave me some insight in to my own situation, and helped to keep me focused, and persevere with the charges. I believe that I met Yvonne for a reason, to give me the education I so desperately needed to see me through. It has given me tremendous confidence to know I have a higher power working with me. I began to listen to these messages and at last I can now understand. I have learnt to acknowledge Shane when he communicates, and I ask for his help and guidance on specific situations in my life. I would get replies and messages sometimes in the forms of dreams, which Yvonne showed us how to interpret. Dreams come in the form of symbols, and hence seem meaningless, but with the tools learnt from the class I was able to reflect on these symbols and understand the messages being sent to me.

To help me through the trauma I was experiencing I took a break to Spain with a friend, leaving my two daughters with my husband for a week. One night, desperately homesick I called my husband from Spain quite emotional. When he came off the phone, he heard a child crying downstairs. Assuming it was our youngest daughter who was just two at the time, he went downstairs to see what was wrong. There was nobody downstairs at all, but when entering the kitchen he noticed that the shed light had been turned on at the bottom of our garden. The shed was locked, and there was no access to our garden except through our house. Nobody had been down there; my husband went to turn the light off quite unsettled!

I told Yvonne what had happened and she said the back garden is the past. The shed represents a person who has the tools needed to put the garden (life) in order. My husband Jon was alerted to this shed by the child crying. She said the child was symbolic of the spiritual side of me that needed nurturing in order to grow. I was moving on, as the light was now on and I had the tools needed to cultivate my life and put the past in order. The fact that Jon had this experience meant he was open to spirit influence as well. That confirmed my theory that my lovely husband Jon had been sent to me. Spirit workers had influenced him towards me.

Another time, I went to turn the switch on for our garden lighting, and accidentally switched the water fountain switch which had never worked; the water started flowing as though it had worked for years! This was symbolic of my life now flowing. I started really trying to use this new found guidance, and begun asking for help in my life. Since the classes, things have turned around for me to the absolute extreme!

Before I met Yvonne, I had quit my job because I was continually breaking down. I felt suicidal, alone, isolated and my mind was completely fragmented. I would put the kettle on and forget I had done it. Every chore was such an effort and we were living in chaos. I generally felt as though I had no direction.

One of my problems was the CPS were taking such a long time to say if my abuser would stand trial. The Police Officer assigned to me was given lots of false dates for a decision. He would pass this date on to me, and I would live for that time. When the date arrived, I would wait for the phone to ring and towards late afternoon would finally call him. It was a real effort for me to do this, as I always felt a nuisance. I would then be told the CPS was postponing their decision, as they had to have further evidence from Social Services.

I lived on a heightened alert and used to think if they didn't prosecute my abuser I would kill myself. I was desperate to have my day in court, never mind what the outcome may be. In September 2004 I had a dream. I was with Shane and he said to me, 'Julia you will hear from the CPS early November and it will be a positive result. Things will move very quickly after that, and I will be with you all the way'. I rang Yvonne and she told me, 'Julia, this will be a test of your faith. You have to put this out of your mind and know you'll have news in November. Do you trust Shane?' and I said 'Yes' and she said, 'Well prove it to him by getting on with your life, focus on the here and now knowing you have a power with you that is tremendous.' I told Shane I had received his guidance and just as Yvonne advised, I put all thoughts of the case out of my mind. My Police Officer rang me on the 3 November and said, 'Julia, the CPS is prosecuting on thirteen counts!'

I realise that the police and the CPS have worked so hard on my behalf and I am truly grateful to them. I also realise Shane is working very hard on my behalf and to me that is wonderful. I feel so supported. Now – even though I am still waiting to give evidence at trial, I have enrolled at college and I'm in the process of applying to University to do a degree in midwifery (somebody has to welcome all those new spirits into the world!)

Everything I face in life, I ask Shane for his input and guidance, and I know if it's the right thing for me, he will help me through it and guide me along the way. The support and reassurance the spiritual knowledge has given me has been life-changing. It is of greater benefit than visiting a medium every week as I used to! I can now work with spirit myself, and know that there is someone there for me however low things may get!

I now realise that people don't come here on earth to be hurt or abused, but everyone on this earth has free will. A child's free will is obviously to a much lesser extent, but certainly as adults we decide how we want to live our lives. Although what happened in my childhood was not my destiny, I now have the power to capitalise on those experiences, and turn that negative into a positive by helping others. This is something I passionately want to do, and I now have the strength to achieve it.

I know that there are other people out there who feel lost and helpless and I aim to some day use the knowledge I have acquired to help them. I have started writing my life story and want to get it out there for people to understand what abuse is like for the child, and the devastating impact it has on their lives. I would also love to counsel victims and have taken my first counselling exam and have passed with flying colours!

LOIS'S STORY

My name is Lois and recently, facing my thirties, I felt it was time to take a positive step forward with my life. Work was not brilliant I felt something was missing. I needed some time out to gain perspective on my world. I decided to look for a meditation class in Cardiff, but couldn't find anything that appealed. It all seemed a bit 'strange and new age', until a friend gave me a booklet and in it was Yvonne's details. I don't know why her advertisement stood out more than any other, but from her photo she looked like a bubbly and warm individual, and more importantly she looked 'normal', and I wanted normal!

I called and arranged a meeting and we met. We talked, or rather she talked, and she told me things that only I knew about my family and friends. She also picked up on a tragedy that had only happened a few weeks earlier to a close friend of mine who had just lost his son in a horrific accident. She told me about her classes for spiritual development, and so out of curiosity I went. Once there I found myself in a class full of like-minded people of all ages and backgrounds. Through a number of lessons we were taught to open our minds, and realise there is more to us and this world than meets the eye. Most people are intrigued by the thought of an afterlife, who are we and why are we here. I now realise we are here to learn, and we all have a purpose.

The classes have given me the tools to work out the rest of my journey as an individual. It also taught me to respect other people even more, as we have all made a decision to come here to earth. Following the classes I decided to study a Reiki one course, and this year I will be finishing Reiki two. My interest in healing and energy work has grown, and to be able to offer energy healing to my family and friends has enriched all our lives. Since stepping into these classes last year I can truly say that my life has changed for the better. I have more confidence in myself and my abilities and a stronger direction in my life. I would like to say a very big thank you to you Yvonne for opening my mind to other possibilities; I have found my direction and feel the happier for it.

MARY'S STORY

My Name is Mary and I have been married for thirty years to David, and we have three children. Throughout my life I have had spiritual experiences. Once I was in America on holiday with my husband and two sons (before I had my daughter). I woke up during the night and saw my mother standing between the two beds. I sat up and said to her, 'Mam how did you get here?', she said to me, 'I can go anywhere now, it's great!'. She was so happy that I started laughing. She looked about forty-years of age with her ginger hair. I asked her 'How?' because she had never been abroad in her life, and she reached down and picked up a coil of luminous green silvery rope which she said was ectoplasm. Now my mother wouldn't have known that word. I woke up the next morning and said to Dave, something has happened to my mother, she was here last night. We had been in Florida nearly three weeks, and when we got home my mother was dead and buried. She was sixty-two years old. I believe she came to soften the blow.

Five and a half months later my sister Isabell, who was two years younger than me, died from bowel cancer. She didn't smoke or drink; she was thirty-four years of age with two children. She had a boy aged eight and a girl aged one year. I was nearly suicidal afterwards. She had been ill over Christmas and died 15 January 1990. I went to bed one night and was crying. I was talking to God and said, 'I want to die, if you want me to stay give me a reason for living.' In February 1990 I discovered I was pregnant with Suzannah. I didn't want any more children but realised this was it; this was my reason to go on and not to end it all. I called her Suzannah Isabell after my sister Isabell.

When Suzannah was about eighteen months, I woke up and knew I had been with my sister Isabell in the night. I was walking along an empty road holding Suzannah by the hand. I

179

seemed to know where I was going. Then I saw my sister waiting for me. I reached her and she was so happy to see us, and I was thrilled to see her. She was looking at Suzannah and laughing. I said to her, 'Do you know I called her after you?', and she nodded. She didn't speak to us or touch us, and I turned to walk away with Suzannah. I said, 'Do you come to see us sometimes too?' and she just nodded. Since then I've seen my sisters face many times, smiling at me with her hair cut and highlighted different to when she died.

I think no one can break the bonds of love and love never dies. I woke up one night and an aunt of mine, who had recently died, was sitting on my bed and she was wearing a grey coat and had a hat on her head. I said I would have to let her daughter know she'd been with me. However, I didn't inform my cousin as we were brought up as Catholics and my aunt would have thought this was the work of the devil. Two weeks later she was back sitting on my bed, so I knew I had to inform her daughter that she was okay. I sent a letter to her in Scotland and she phoned me to find out what had happened. I told her, 'Your mother told me the coat I saw her wearing was her favourite'. I wouldn't have known what clothes she had as they all live so far away. My cousin told me she was devastated over her mum's death, but once she spoke to me she felt okay.

I met Yvonne through my son, as he works with someone who had gone on one of her courses. My birthday was approaching and on the day before I said to spirit, 'Come on, I will be fifty- three tomorrow, when am I going to develop further?' That evening my son came to visit and told me about the classes and invited me along. I jumped at the chance, and it was the best thing I had ever done.

I now realise I have been guided through life. The opening and closing exercises I learnt in the class have taught me to switch off, and I am far more in control of me as a result of this. One night when my eyes were closed, I saw on my eyelids an African person looking at me and the name Benjamin came into my mind. I saw his face as if he was standing in front of me.

Another time I was linking in and I asked for a sign that would let me know someone was with me. A flash of lightening lit up the room, and I felt overawed at this power that was working with me. The little lamp in my bedroom constantly comes on without my pressing the switch, and I hear footsteps going up and down the stairs. The television also turns on and off by itself, and changes channels without anyone touching the remote control. I asked for a sign for my husband, and a Christmas hat that was on a shelf started flashing. I love having these amazing happenings and Yvonne came into my life at a time when I needed help. She has helped me to see the bigger picture.

MATTHEW'S STORY

My name is Matthew and I am a thirty-year-old single male. I live and work in London, and I am a Croupier in a West End casino. I was born in Cardiff and I am the youngest of four boys. I grew up on a council estate and my dad was a lorry driver and my mum was a housewife. My mother suffered with her nerves and she and I were very close. My father was aggressive and drank a lot.

From a young age I always felt different to everyone around me. My brothers respected and looked up to my father whereas I didn't; I was more for my mother. I was very feminine and had no aggression in me. My brothers and school friends taunted me, calling me 'poof, queer, gay lord' and so on. I had no understanding about gender and sexuality; it was others that first brought this to my attention with their continual baiting.

When I got to puberty I realised I had homosexual tendencies. I became paranoid and knew others were taunting me because they recognised this. I felt ashamed and disgusted and tried so hard to hide my femininity, so that I could fit in.

When I was about sixteen I used to hang out with a crowd of people, which included Kris, Yvonne's son. We would all go to Kris's house and whereas the others would be upstairs, I used to be with Yvonne in the kitchen. She would be cooking or ironing and I would sit and chat with her. I was still in denial at this time, hiding my true feelings. Yvonne and I became friends and I would sometimes call at Kris's house to see his mum and I would talk with her. I used to ask her about the spirit world, as I had always been interested in this subject. I had an imaginary friend when I was young, and I sensed my late grandfather around me. He was a comforting presence, and at night times I used to fall to sleep knowing he was with me. At this time I had a girlfriend and although it was a platonic relationship, it was the perfect foil for me. When that relationship finished I knew I had to confront myself.

One night I went with a group of girlfriends to a club. Although we didn't know it, this was a club for gays. That night changed my life, and I knew without any doubt I was gay. The next day I rang Yve and told her I needed to talk. I arrived at the house and I said 'There is something I want to tell you, but I am afraid you will think I am dirty. Please don't look at me when I am telling you', and I stood with my back to her and told her 'I am gay'. Yve told me not to beat myself up for whom or what I was. She said she had known I was gay from the moment she met me. She told me 'Matthew this is a hard road for you to travel but "no pain, no gain", and it will work out fine, just as it was always intended'.

I went home that day and told my family. It was really hard to do and I felt a sense of shame, but I couldn't hide any more. My mother and one of my brothers' were fine, but another brother thought I would molest his children, and my father thought I was going though a phase.

I was now able to live my life as a gay male, and took the brave step of telling those around me. I went to development classes with Yve, and used to go to the healing clinic at her house. The spiritual influence and guidance helped me tremendously.

One day I was walking to my house and was a few yards away when an ordinary looking man walked towards me. Even though it was daylight, and for no apparent reason, I felt nervous. He stopped me and asked for a 'fag' and I said 'I haven't got any fags sorry'. He said 'Did you call me a fag?' and then punched me full in the face. When this happened it was like deja vu. The man was much bigger than me but there was a feeling of calmness with me. It was like I was on automatic pilot, and I turned and walked to my house.

Once inside, the injustice of what had happened struck me, but I was really puzzled to realise I knew this was going to happen. A few weeks later in the development class, a student did a reading for me and said 'Your grandfather is saying you have been hit in the face, and it wasn't deja vu as he had shown you this attack in a dream, to prepare you. He is saying you were taught a valuable lesson, and to always use your instincts. If you ever feel threatened you must act on the feeling and move away from the threat.' I have never forgotten this, and there have been occasions when I have put this advice to good practice.

I have learnt to speak in my head to my guardian angel, whose name is George. I ask him for guidance and influence and he answers me in different ways. I have to work hard to interpret the guidance, and it comes in many forms. I have dreams which are full of symbols, there are always lots of coincidences and sometimes things just fall into place.

Before I moved to London I repeatedly asked George for help, to get me to be where I was supposed to be. I listened to the guidance and here I am, living and working in London. I love my life. I am comfortable with who I am, and realise I am as nature intended me to be. It has been a hard road, but it is a road I have gladly travelled. I have had lots of pain but the gain has been tremendous.

PAULA'S STORY

I initially visited Yve with a friend who was suicidal. I'd been on 'suicide watch' for a couple of weeks, and couldn't take anymore. My friend had tried counselling, and she was prescribed drugs by the doctor, but nothing was working. I suggested she visit a medium, and discovered Yve! I saw her advertisement and it mentioned trauma, and spiritual guidance. Surely this had to work?

I made the appointments, and we turned up not knowing what to expect. We were shown into a really large kitchen and we sat around a table, and talked and talked. Yve made us tea and before we knew it a couple of hours had past. I thought we were running out of time and we wouldn't get our readings, but I needn't have worried. Yve asked who was to be first and my friend went upstairs to the lounge where the readings are done. When it was my turn I was impressed by my reading, but was particularly intrigued by the spiritual education we had heard about. We left Yve's house promising to visit again.

A few months later I met the 'man of my dreams'. He pursued me relentlessly, and as soon as I let down my guard and became involved with him, he changed and dumped me.

This was a repeated pattern for me. I rang Yve, and arranged an appointment. Little did I know how much that phone call was going to change my life, both spiritually and mentally.

I arrived at Yve's, and she said the words that were soon to become wonderfully familiar to me, 'Hiya my babes'. I was ushered into her calming upstairs room, and dissolved into tears, but felt better already. I think I even remarked I didn't need the reading now! I had always had a problem with men; not the meeting them, oh no, that bit was fine; it was just the type and the duration that were the problem. Believe you me, I'd had them all! Drug dealers, a murderer, orphans, anyone with psychological problems, they all came to me. I had no idea why.

There was me a bright, vivacious (some might say cocky and loud!) girl, up for a laugh, but attracting all these damaged people. I was well educated, and had an MA in sociology. I worked as a project manager for a multi-national telecommunications company, I owned my own house, had a sporty car and yet here I was in bits. Well, I was now on the way to finding out why!

Yve picked up on the reason for my visit straight away, and was very to the point, blunt even in getting her message across. She told me I had a repetitive and negative pattern of behaviour, and I was dysfunctional. She said I had low self esteem and I was attracting people that would feed my dysfunction. She told me the mind is like a database and from babyhood, everything in our environment is keyed in to the mind, filed and saved. The information we absorb will affect us in different ways, depending on our date of birth – as the planets are an energy influence – and our soul growth.

She asked me if I could see auras, and I told her no. She showed me how to see hers, and I was amazed. Yve said as we think so we pulsate and this pulsation forms our aura.

She said our aura was like a jigsaw puzzle, and I was attracting people to me that fit. I couldn't understand what she was telling me, and so she brought in her flipchart and drew it for me. Now I got it! Like attracts like, I was dysfunctional, and so I was attracting dysfunction to me, and the dysfunction I was attracting was the reverse to my dysfunction. Yve explained to alter this repetitive pattern of behaviour I needed to change what was in the database of my mind, and I had to start with how I saw me.

She then told me my granddad was with us. He gave lovely evidence that it was him. My granddad had been my world, but he had passed sixteen-years previously. It was like having him stood in the room, but he wasn't on his own. He had a J initial with him, the number three was significant, and also a problem with blood. I just couldn't work out who it was. Yve kept mentioning different things which I was dismissing. Instead of pushing the point, Yve just casually said it would come to me, but I wasn't to ignore it, as it was obviously important.

She explained she was being given the information mind to mind, via waves of the air. Sometimes the information would be interrupted by the waves, and then she would only get a small part of the communication. This was why she couldn't pick up the full name. At the end of the reading I realised it was my long- term friend James who had died of a brain haemorrhage three years previous. After the reading we sat chatting and the phone rang. Yve excused herself and I heard her make an appointment for what was presumably another damaged soul. She sat back down and I told her I wanted to know more about – well, what Yve was all about.

When chatting she had mentioned to me about spirit communication being subtle and cryptic. All the experiences I'd had growing up now had meaning, and I realised I wasn't alone in stuff I had felt, heard or thought I'd seen. Not only was I not alone, these experiences meant something. I had to have my spiritual education and booked my first lesson for the next Wednesday evening, I couldn't wait. Although I told her I wanted private lessons, on the Saturday Yve rang to ask if I minded someone else joining us. I asked her who, and it was only the person that had phoned at the end of my reading!

On the Wednesday I was introduced to Jason and it was like meeting a friend, someone I'd known forever. I wasn't alone; there were other people out there that had the same experiences as me. Embarking on the education changed my life, changed me, and all my relationships. I'm happier, not so gullible, I'm more comfortable with me and I now know my worth. I have a tool kit for dealing with life. All my past experiences are stored in my mind and I can access them when there needed. Part of my education was learning and understanding symbols. I can analyse the guidance given in my sleep state and all my family and friends ring me with their dreams.

I thought I was the only person who had a TV with a mind of its own. I felt sorry for the TV repair man who had to come and transport my huge widescreen TV to be repaired because of the interference/wavy lines/lime green screen/turning itself on and off. He plugged in my replacement and I telephoned him later to say the brand new replacement was doing exactly the same thing as the TV he was repairing. The symbol of the television is communication, communication accessed via other channels or things of the air. The colour lime green is representative of working with the mind. I had started to access other channels by working with the mind. My TV repair man came back three weeks later with a strange look in his eye, and a note that said there was nothing wrong with my television! I have hung that note in my lounge for everyone to see.

Accepting I now have the ability to work with the universal power is incredible. I started on this path for purely selfish reasons, but now I am helping others to help themselves. My suicidal girlfriend had been the initial reason for seeing Yve. I am happy to say she now realises her worth, and I have spent many hours with her explaining about life. I have faith in my ability, and I've been able to answer so many questions from so many people since being taught, and that makes it very worthwhile.

SHARON'S STORY

My name is Sharon and I am a married woman with four beautiful children. I work as a team leader for a leading insurance company and I am also attending college to learn hairdressing. I am always on the go, my life is really busy and I am a proper 'people person'. Just recently life has taken on a new meaning and this is because I met Yve. My maternal grandmother had died, and my mother was inconsolable. She desperately needed to know that my grandmother still lived on in spirit.

I tried to arrange a reading with many mediums all were either out or unavailable that is, all except Yve. My sister Kelly, mum and I arrived at her home, and she called us in to the kitchen. We talked about spirit and Yve told us we were there for more than just a reading, and if we wanted to have spiritual education then we could join her class. I was really excited as this could finally give me answers to some of the experiences that puzzled me, and it would hopefully help me progress further.

I was already a way down the spiritual road, and as far back as I can remember I loved anything to do with the afterlife. I always had an inner knowing. When I went to high school my friends noticed I knew things, and they would try and test any physic ability by asking about colours and numbers they were thinking about. A lot of times I was successful at these tests and I was known then as 'the witch'. As I grew older I became more interested in why I would get feelings about people or situations. At sixteen I lost my paternal grandmother and this was the most traumatic time of my life. I loved my nan more than life itself and was devastated by her death. I kept wondering where she was, and I sensed her around me.

The easiest way to contact the spirit world for myself was by tarot cards. You can buy a pack and there are written instructions telling you what to do. So that was it, I took up tarot reading. I practiced on family and friends but sometimes I would see people who had passed. Other times I would feel warmth and experience different sensations but I didn't know what it meant and I didn't know how to turn this gift on or off. The experiences were interesting but I yearned to learn more, I just didn't know who to turn to.

I was always helping people, I could be walking in town and I would know exactly where I was going and then all of a sudden I would find I'd taken a wrong turning and wasn't aware of it at the time. I might then see someone I hadn't seen for years, we'd get chatting and they would tell me they were having difficulties and off I'd go, offering comfort and guidance. I used to think this was very strange.

I attended the classes and I learnt I was in service to spirit and the universe. Like a piece on a chessboard I had been moved to help someone who was in my vicinity. I was in the right place at the right time, and spirit workers had influenced me to give help and comfort where needed. The education classes have changed my life and that of those around me. As soon as I started the classes I experienced lots of light bulbs popping and the television would go on and off. The only question my husband had for me was "Do we get a refund for the light bulbs?" To this day my portable TV in my room still flashes lime green and pink!

I have learnt so much about life and I want to help people. I told my guardian angel this, and one day I was in work when suddenly I felt drawn to one of my colleagues. Yve had taught us we must be disciplined, but I was at the stage of being like a kid, and wasn't able to leave well alone. I decided to link and find out if there was a reason for me feeling this way. I stood next to my colleague and he looked puzzled, as I had this strange smile. He said 'Why are you smiling, come on then what do you want?' He assumed I was going to ask him to do me a favor.

In my mind I could see a man, tall with a rather large belly in a pair of jeans, he also had what I can only describe as scruffy hair at the back of his head. I told my colleague what I could see and immediately he said 'that's my step- dad'. He had passed about four months ago. The main thing the man was showing me was blue eyes. However my colleague said he had brown eyes. He was so taken back by the visit; he telephoned his mum straight away.

After a few minutes he came back and looked quite tearful. I asked if everything was okay. He told me that his mum had put out a cry to the universe that day, as she had not had any signs from her husband that he had passed over and was okay; she was so upset not knowing. Then my colleague said 'You know you said his eyes were blue, well my mum had not told anyone this, but on his death bed he sat up, looked at my mum and his eyes turned blue and then he was gone'. This was obviously the confirmation that his mum needed and it felt great to have made someone happy.

Having done 'my bit' I thought I had better go outside the building and close down. However I didn't get the chance. When I got outside I bumped into one of my friends' from work, suddenly I could see a man, not much hair, in a bottle green jumper and old jeans too short on the legs. He had a pair of black shoes on instead of trainers. This turned out to be my friend's step-dad. When she spoke to her mum she laughed, as that's all he would wear, green jumpers and black loafer-type shoes.

Each week in class we would discuss our events and spiritual happenings, and I was so amazed and excited at my development. I love receiving spirit messages and realise I was born to do spiritual work. I have met the person that works with me from the world of spirit. Her name is Serena, and she regularly gives me guidance through dreams and thoughts. I have learnt to interpret the symbols she sends me, and all my friends come to me to have their dreams analysed.

My work colleagues and college friends have been queuing up for me to give them readings but I would tell them to wait until I had completed the course. Yve encouraged us to practice, and so when the time was right I decided to do some readings and put my new skills to the test. The date was arranged and myself and Wendy from the class turned up at the house of a lady who was an acquaintance from college. She had invited friends who also wanted readings. Although Yve didn't know it, I had taken my tarot cards with me, as I was frightened I wouldn't be successful using my mind.

I sat with my first sitter and dealt the cards. Within minutes I could see a lady with a waistcoat on and her hair tied back in a pony tail. The lady kept saying, 'That's my baby' to me. I told my sitter and she was so pleased, as she believed this was her mother who had died when she was only three-years-old. She had been to many mediums but her mum had never come through. The reason for her saying 'That's my baby' was because my sitter was the youngest child.

Needless to say the reading was a great success and I felt confident to do the next reading.

This reading was quite emotional. My sitter's father connected with me and he gave lovely evidence. Her dad was the backbone of the family and they had all crumbled following his death. He told me I must help his daughter both spiritually and academically, as apparently she was on the verge of giving up college because she was dyslexic. I told her what he said and she confirmed it was true. I immediately offered my services to her. She felt so much better knowing her father was still looking out for her, and she is doing great in college now.

Wendy also had a great time that evening and she was really successful with her work and she wasn't using tarot cards. We told Yve all about the evening and I confessed I had used the tarot. Yve said, 'Sharon, you don't need tools or a focus to work with spirit. You are quite capable of using your mind. Can you imagine if the only way spirit could get through to you was if you had your tarot cards with you, you'd be no good as a chess piece for them'. I understood her point and from now on, the tarot are a thing of the past.

I am a spiritual medium not a tarot reader, and I now know there is a big difference. I have the confidence to work without a prop. Recently I took Wendy with me to do readings for my work colleagues and I left the cards at home, firmly locked away. I am pleased to say the evening was a great success.

WENDY'S STORY

My name is Wendy and I'm forty-two years of age. My upbringing has been pretty ordinary, my dad's a builder and my mum's a housewife. I have two sisters and a brother and we were brought up in Splott in Cardiff. I grew up with lots of guidance and love. At the age of twenty I met the man of my dreams – gorgeous Greg. We married two years later and had two sons Gregory and Antoni. They have grown to be very special young men. They argue and fight of course, and they play their music much too loud. They are typical teenagers really, and although they drive me crazy sometimes, I wouldn't be without them.

I have always been the type of person people talk to. Friends and family confide in me, and people I don't know seem to be drawn to me, on the bus, hospital waiting rooms etc., and every job I've ever had has been interacting with people.

I first met Yvonne a few months after Greg died. He had been ill for several years and eventually the Doctors and Specialists gave him six months to live, but he lived two years (he was always stubborn). He was my soul mate, and I was in bits when he died. My two sons were just fifteen and eighteen and were totally destroyed.

I don't know where I got the strength but I quickly set about arranging his funeral. I literally interviewed ministers and vicars, I knew how I wanted it to be and didn't want some guy reading from a book and forgetting Greg's name (I have been to a few of those). I had to talk my boys through a funeral; they had never been to one before. I explained the process from start to finish; this in itself was very hard. My boys showed so much courage and maturity. I took them out and bought suits and shoes, and I went through every detail with them.

On the day of the funeral the house was full of people but my boys were my main concern. We got to the church and walked behind the coffin down the aisle to Ava Cassidy's 'Fields of Gold'. There were over three hundred people there. I remember thinking 'All these people from different parts of Greg's life', I felt so sad and so proud at the same time.

193

The service went exactly as I wanted, the minister was wonderful and my dad got up and spoke beautiful words that will stay with me all my life. As the service came to an end a beam of bright sunshine seemed to shoot down onto the coffin. I could hear people gasp. 'Some where Over the Rainbow' by Ava Cassidy was playing and I knew he did that, and thought 'Trust you Greg you had to get their attention.' He was always a showoff.

About a month before Greg died I was woken from my sleep, and I heard very clearly a woman's voice say to me 'the end of April'. I sat up in my bed, looked around the room and instinctively knew this was a spiritual happening. I turned to Greg who was sleeping by my side; kissed him on the head and thought 'Oh my God, we have four weeks.' I didn't doubt this for a second, even though he was quite well at that point. As the days passed he got steadily worse, and he eventually died at home in his sleep on 24 April 2004. He was forty-six and this truly was the saddest day of my life.

A few months passed and I started to accept his death, no one else did really, but I just knew he wasn't gone. I couldn't explain it, I wasn't in denial, I just knew there was more to life. One night a dear friend of mine Sharon, was talking to me about the spiritual education classes she had started attending. I was intrigued and she arranged for me to go with her to the next class.

This is where my incredible journey began. I met Yvonne and 'WOW' she is the most practical, down-to-earth person I've ever met. She has changed my life forever. She gave me my spiritual education and I wish I had known from childhood everything I know now. It would have made such a difference to my life. I believe the education should be available to everyone.

Working with symbols has been mind blowing, and it's funny to think they've always been there. I now realise there has been a plan for my life, and I was meant to be the people person I am. Since finishing my education I've continued to be the friend I always have been and I'm still listening to the stranger on the bus, sympathizing with their life story, only this time I know I've got help!! It has enriched not just my life but also my boys' lives. I believe I was guided to Yvonne for a purpose.

In late November I was stood with my sister at my husband's grave. She remarked on the bright orange, plastic butterfly that my son Antoni had asked me to place there a few months earlier. Out of what seemed thin air, a real bright orange butterfly appeared in front of my face, flew slowly down my body and landed on my leg. It stayed there for quite some time and I was speechless. The symbol for the butterfly is transition, transition from one life to another. I knew Greg was showing me this, and I was elated. My sister turned to me and said, 'That was so weird, were did it come from? You never see a butterfly in late November'.

I called Yve straight away as I just had to share this special moment with her. I now know that symbols are a universal language and they are there for all of us to use. Those in spirit communicate in cryptic and subtle ways and symbols are part of this communication. I now listen to everything around me. I have used my knowledge to help people, friends and family. Sometimes they ring me to analyse their dreams, and they are amazed when I work on the symbols for them. It gives me such a buzz to help people. So many things have happened to me since Greg's death.

Before he died we both decided on a code for him to use, to give me evidence he had survived death. I am still waiting for that code, and I am confident he's waiting to pick his moment, but in other ways he has definitely let me know he's around and believe me, he's had a ball!! He constantly switches the TV over, especially when I'm watching East Enders or Big Brother. These were programs he disliked. My lights flicker all the time, songs come on the radio just as I'm thinking of him, and for a while stones were being thrown at my windows. I was convinced it was children playing about outside. I would open my front door instantly and no one would be there.

One night I was at class and I was saying Greg had not yet given me our code and Yve said, 'He may not have given you the code, but he says to tell you it's him throwing the stones at your windows'. I couldn't believe what she had said. I hadn't told a soul this was happening, and it hasn't happened since, as Greg had got his message across.

Since he's been gone, he even tried to get me a job at Greggs the Bakers!! When he was alive he always joked saying it was his shop, and he went there on a daily basis. He always came home saying the same thing 'I just popped into my shop'. Not long after he died I bumped in to an old friend of mine. After a quick catch up she told me she had just got a job at 'Greggs the Bakers' and they were looking for more staff.

I had never worked in a bakery before but was intrigued, maybe just because it was GREGGS. She arranged an interview for me, and when I received the appointment I couldn't believe it. The interview was to be held in the building where Greg and I had first met twenty-five years before, only then it was a clothes shop and I was a sales assistant. 'That was weird' I thought. I went along and the place hadn't changed much and I got the job. The induction day was an eye-opener. It was held in the room that used to be Greg's office, when he was the manager. All of this showed to me beyond any doubt the power of spirit, and there is no such thing as coincidence. I had been taken down memory lane and the memories were lovely.

I am putting my spiritual education to good use. A friend of mine came to see me the other day. She had dreamt of her mother's garden, and she had planted beautiful flowers and shrubs for her mother. When she visited the garden was empty, every thing was gone. My friend was clearly troubled by the dream. I explained the garden represents your life, full garden full life, for example; she had constantly tried to enrich her mother's life over many years but her mother hadn't appreciated it. All the good she had tried to do was being wasted, as her mother made no effort. Her mother's life has been plagued by mental illness, and my dear friend's life had not been an easy one because of it.

I was able to help one lovely lady who came to me for a reading. During the reading I picked up that her previous marriage had not been a good one, and that her first husband had killed himself in an awful way. She had re-married but her second marriage was suffering because of the overwhelming guilt and sadness of her first marriage. I am pleased to say I was able to help her move past it. It was a very moving experience for her and for me, and made me realise how important this work is.

I have done many readings since then and each time I always feel truly uplifted when I've been able to help. Don't get me wrong, it isn't always easy walking the spiritual path. Sometimes people and even family members can be very patronizing. They say things like, 'Well if it makes you feel better' or 'What ever gets you through.' I often feel quite sad when that happens, sad for them that they don't get it. If only they listened to what is going on around them.

I am from a working-class background and I didn't do great at school, but I wouldn't change anything about my life except for losing Greg. With my new-found knowledge I know now that we are all on a journey, and it's not the end or the beginning, we are in the middle but it's a beautiful journey and I want to enjoy the ride.

I will always be grateful to Sharon for taking me quite literally by the hand to the classes; and Yve for all she has taught me and the friend she has become; the wonderful people I have met who will all be a part of my life forever.

I have left the stories of two particular students till last. Ann and Claire are a mother and daughter, and when you have read what they have to say, an explanation is needed by me. I will hand you over to them.

ANN'S STORY

My name is Ann and I am married to Bryan. We have two children, Mike and Claire. Mike lives with his partner Jemma and they have a baby, our adored grandson Dylan. Claire lives at home with Bryan and me. A series of coincidences led us to Yvonne, and we first met her six months ago. I was given an emergency appointment to take Claire to meet her. Claire was so poorly, suicidal, and both she and I were at the end of our tethers!

Claire had been a troubled teenager and was very unhappy. I would constantly ask her if she was being bullied but she would deny this. In the Christmas holidays of 2002, Claire woke me one night at three in the morning and handed me a letter she had written. It was covered in dry tears and what I read had a devastating impact on me, Claire was on the verge of committing suicide. I rushed with Claire to our family Doctor and he immediately wrote to the child and family clinic asking for urgent help.

We waited weeks to hear anything and I telephoned our Doctor weekly, and he phoned the hospital weekly. After about two months Claire was given an appointment to see a specialist, and he prescribed an antipsychotic drug and said Claire was very poorly. Claire was given weekly follow up appointments and her medication was changed constantly, as she had so many awful side effects.

One day the Doctor told us about an Adolescent Unit at a local Psychiatric Hospital. It was recommended Claire go there for a short stay, so she could have twenty-four hours observation. Bryan and I took Claire to the unit for what was supposed to be a two weeks stay and she stayed there for nine months. Although she was on many pills each day, including anti depressant and anti psychotic, she was still very poorly, self harming and very suicidal. Bryan and I would visit with her daily.

After nine months, when she came home from the hospital, she was then under the supervision of a special team. We visited the doctors every few weeks and usually once a week a nurse called and spent an hour with her. She was diagnosed with Obsessive Compulsive Disorder and Schizophrenia, but none of the normal medication had helped her at all. Claire suffered tremendous side effects from them, including putting on nine stones of weight.

I eventually discovered Claire had heard voices since she was four-years-old. She thought it was normal and didn't tell anyone, assuming they were imaginary friends. With her growing up, the voices became multiple and more derogatory. The voices were ruining her life. School had been horrendous in the local comprehensive. She was a loner and was bullied because of that. The voices drowned out the teachers voices, but they weren't an actual sound, more like a loud thought, but the thought would be shouting.

It was so distressing for me to find out my beautiful daughter had suffered in silence. She had to take her GCSE's at home, although by that time she was already in the hospital. I had to fetch her home for the exams then take her back in.

When we met Yvonne it was 4 July, 2004, and we went to her home. Claire was sent downstairs to have energy healing by one of the student's, whilst Yvonne explained Claire's situation to me. When Claire joined us after her healing, Yvonne started counselling her. Yvonne assured Claire that the voices were not her, but negative earth bound spirits who were drawn to her because of her psychic abilities, low self esteem and low vibrations. These spirits were playing with her mind, controlling her every move so that she constantly harmed herself. It was like a horror film – I felt like we were playing characters except that this was for real. When I looked into Claire's eyes, she wasn't there!

Anyway, we saw Yvonne twice a week and at these sessions Claire would have healing to boost her energy levels, and then counselling. Yvonne would drip feed Claire information, giving her time to understand what was being said. She used a flip chart to help emphasise what she was teaching. Every week Yvonne would reinforce the things she had said to Claire previously, but would always add something new for Claire to think about. She handed over responsibility for Claire's recovery to Claire herself.

The voices got worse before they got better – the spirits knew their time was up – they had been found out, and were slowly repelled as Claire began to believe in Yvonne and herself at last! This raised her vibrations. Yvonne said 'imagine a desert island surrounded by water, and the seas are flat. Someone swimming to that island would have no problem reaching it. Then imagine waves starting to come from that island, the person swimming to it would be pushed back'. Claire was the island and the water was her thought waves.

The swimmer was an earth bound spirit. Claire's way of thinking was low and flat because she had been depressed for so long, and suffered with low self esteem and that was how these negative spirit voices were able to reach her. Yvonne explained what was in Claire's database or mind needed to be altered. She needed to change her whole way of thinking, including how Claire saw herself. She needed to become positive and this would alter her vibrations.

Every week Yvonne would speak with Claire and explain about life. She talked about how every one of us was capable of making negative judgments about other people. She made Claire realise she herself was capable of this. Yvonne would then make Claire understand each one of us had to be robust enough to withstand the times when others judged us in this way. We had to learn to love ourselves, and be confident with who we are. We must never, ever let others make us feel bad about ourselves.

Yvonne said Claire is a very spiritual person and hopefully eventually would be able to work alongside Yvonne, helping people who were experiencing the things she had experienced. After a few weeks Claire and I joined Yvonne's spiritual education classes. They were eye-opening and very informative. Claire continued to have her healing and counselling. She came off all her medication, and told the doctors that she wouldn't need them again. She is now taking vitamins as advised by a friend of Yvonne's, and they have been much more help than all her prescribed medication.

As we learned about spiritual education our eyes were opened, as were our minds. It was breathtaking! All the things I had wondered about during my life, Yvonne had answers for. Claire became more confident week by week and she had frequent psychic experiences. Through Yvonne's counselling, Claire's vibrations got stronger and she was able to push her negative voices further away from her, until at last they were gone. After thirteen years of chaos, came peace!

We were amazed to learn about earth bound spirits. We were taught we all existed before we came to earth, and we come here to learn lessons. We each have someone from the spirit world working with us, and their job is to help us achieve what we came here for. We don't have to listen as we have free will. When we die we still have free will, and don't have to move on. If we choose this, we would be earthbound. People might remain earthbound for lots of different reasons, and the majority of people who are in this state are not bad people. Yvonne stressed that children do not become earthbound because spirit workers collect children immediately their spirit is away from the body.

Eventually we all go over, but we could stay in that in between stage for quite some time. However, being earthbound is very restrictive as we no longer have a body, and our mind is still locked. Earthbound spirits only have the same mind power as you and I. They can't move an object to get anyone's attention, but they can speak to someone living in a physical body mind to mind. When these spirits are able to get through to someone in this way, it gives them something to do. If they so wished, they can have a great time.

We are all like radios, each of us emitting our own frequency from the mind, and if that frequency is the same as an earthbound spirits, then they can contact us. This is what happened to Claire, but the ones communicating to Claire were of a lower vibration, in other words not very nice when they lived as people. As Claire was so low herself with depression etc., then there was a perfect match.

Now Claire is concentrating on her music – she has always been gifted. She plays around seven different instruments and has written many songs. Her dream is to become a rock artist. All through her ordeal, her music was her only pleasure. She idolises Axl Rose of Guns N' Roses, and took solace in listening to his lyrics. She would love to meet him and tell him what an inspiration he has been.

Claire is now losing her weight and after passing her driving test first time, she is much more confident and starting to socialise more. Instead of being my little shadow for the past three to four years I hardly see her now! She's changing into a lovely, talented, normal young lady, who is destined for big things. Thank you Yvonne.

CLAIRE'S STORY.

My name is Claire, and I'm Ann's seventeen-year-old daughter. All my life I'd felt like an outcast. I wasn't meant to be here. I'd had voices since as far back as I can remember, and started to realise this wasn't normal when no-one at school was talking about anything like that. I wouldn't say a thing and slowly I realised I was experiencing nothing like anyone else. I could see the people that would talk to me, I could feel their presence if I couldn't see them, and soon they started to put thoughts in my head. Initially these were good things but then these thoughts and images turned into twisted and repulsive things that I would mould my mind too. The thoughts became harder and harder to ignore, and my head would be full up with anger and hatred.

In school I would be continually distracted by these voices and they quickly became my Bible of what I should do every minute of the day. Each day when I woke up I would feel upset that I actually woke in the first place. Then every night after that, I'd wish that my body would slow down so much when I slept that it would just stop. This is where my loneliness and depression started to show.

I would always be asked by everyone if I was okay, but I lied all the time so that I didn't have to face what was happening to me. From then, every word that I spoke, every move that I made, wasn't any of my doing. I felt like I was just watching my life, staring, unable to move. I would start having suicidal thoughts but never acted on them. I felt a small glimmer of hope when I was taken to see a child psychologist. But I came away feeling even lower when told I wasn't depressed and they'd be in touch.

Months passed and finally we managed to make an appointment again with the same person. By this time my head was empty of me and full of 'them' (I call them my demons). My image suffered terribly and there was no taking care of myself by showering, or even wearing different clothes each day. I was prescribed drugs straight away. After a week I felt like they were killing me slowly, dragging me deeper into a black hole.

The weeks went on trying different anti-psychotic drugs, and each week would drag a little something else out into the open. For some reason it had just hit me that I wasn't alone in my head. I was offered a place in a psychiatric unit for two weeks. The two weeks turned into nine months, and helped me confront my problem a little bit but it didn't seem a good idea. I was becoming more interested in death to others and myself, and acted on different impulses regularly. The times where I would have therapy, everyone would look confused. They didn't know what my problem was. I started to write down my thoughts on paper and turn them into poems and lyrics for songs. While in the unit, I gained nine stones from the medication I was taking.

I came out thinking I was a lost cause, I couldn't be helped except for killing myself, which seemed like the easiest way out. But every time I would be stopped by the tiniest thought in my head, and it would somehow break through an unbreakable wall and make me listen. To this day I'm still not sure what it was and can't explain it. I was diagnosed with schizophrenia, paranoia, and OCD (obsessive compulsive disorder).

For the months before this I had been reading spiritual magazines and was getting very interested in them, so I went to a spiritual convention. There I met a clairvoyant called Leo who made me feel powerful over whatever was holding me down. I felt energised after speaking to him, thought nothing else of it but never forgot it. I started to go to a music training provider so that I could see where my music outlet could take me. My new friends would try to cheer me up, but nothing would help.

In the workshop I met a lady called Maureen, who was a former pupil of Yvonne's, and I found out that it could possibly be something else that was in my head. I was introduced to Yvonne as an emergency appointment. The things that she was saying were being rejected by the company in my head. Their thoughts became mine and I didn't know whose thoughts were in my head anymore. I had recently finished a book that had 'coincidentally' fallen into my lap. Yvonne's words matched that of the book, but still I didn't know what to make of it all.

My mother put all her trust in Yvonne, and this encouraged me. I decided to come off all my pills, which was a very hard thing to do. I'd learnt to live with them and now I had to go cold turkey. When I was taken off the pills in the unit, I was climbing the walls and felt neurotic, emotional, and insecure and so on but this time… why wasn't this as bad? I felt a little

205

depressed but my body wasn't rejecting having nothing to control it. It felt healthier.

I was advised to go to Yvonne's spiritual education classes, which initially I found slightly far-fetched. I thought that everyone was brainwashed. However, over the weeks the tiniest things made sense. My experiences and thoughts made sense, and I felt like a door had opened to me that had always been invisible. I was told that my 'demons' were actually earth-bound spirits that found me, broke down my energy and found their way into my head to terrorise it as company for them. I was the toy that they were playing with. There the schizophrenia label was dropped. The spirits knew what was happening and started to fight back. I didn't feel like fighting but got spurred on to try.

Those couple of weeks felt like years and it was the hardest trial I've ever had to face. It took a while to get back to a 'normal' that I'd never experienced before, a peaceful place with only me to answer back. It took some persuading to make me sure that it was just me in my head, as I didn't believe that it was all over. I didn't have time to relax though; Yvonne had plenty of things for me to do, to get my self confidence up, my happiness, and to get my music flowing out of me again.

The music has been the only outlet for me that didn't make me sting and bleed. The only rush I need now is my music when I'm performing it. I'm a different person at that moment, a genuinely happy person deep down. My lyrics may be hard hitting but I wouldn't write them any other way. Otherwise it wouldn't be the truth. Now, I live my life by this experience and it can only make me stronger. Each fall I have only feels like a stumble now. I'm learning to think on my own and learn all over again about the things I had misconceptions about.

I still have bad days, very bad days and even worse days, but I've learnt that I shouldn't take the coward's way out like I always tried too. I've got to ride this to the very end and enjoy whatever I can. I am slowly getting my life back on track now, but I do feel as if I've just been born. Everything's new to me now. I'm seeing the world through eyes that have just opened and I'm ready to live. I just don't feel like I can sit in the house anymore and do nothing. I've got stuff I want to do and don't want to waste any more time.

The parts of me that were slowly being eaten away by my 'demons', I now know will never grow back, but new parts will grow in their place. They will take a while to grow but might be well worth the wait. The old parts of me will always be missed but they are gone now and I have to live with the new ones and learn how to use them. It's like learning to walk again.

Thank you so much Yvonne for being my physiotherapy. X

When my former student Maureen rang to ask if I could see Claire and her Mum urgently, I was a bit dubious. I do not profess to be a miracle worker and I realise mental health and spirit communication can sometimes seem one and the same thing. There are people who suffer a real mental health illness, but there are also people who experience negative spirit communication. I do not credit myself with being able to tell who suffers with what.

When the call came I had two people with me. One was my student, and she was also a healer. The other was a friend called Chris, and she had a pharmacy background. I sat in the quiet and spoke to HQ and asked if I should see Claire. He came into my aura and the energy around me moved to make space for him. I pick this movement up like a feeling of cobwebs on the face. I waited to see if thoughts filtered into my mind but, instead, I had a sensing. I sensed his confirmation, and it is like a mild electric current running through my head and down to the stomach area. I experience this feeling when working with HQ, and have come to interpret it as meaning a positive.

I was not a mental health worker and so, if I could help Claire in a positive way, it must have been because her problem was spiritual. I marvelled at how I had two people on hand who could contribute to the situation in a positive way. I told HQ 'I have no idea how to work with someone hearing negative spirit voices and so you will have to help me.'

When mum and daughter arrived I sent Claire for healing with my student, giving me the opportunity to speak to her mum. I listened to their story and felt such compassion. They had truly been through a nightmare. Chris asked about the medication Claire had been taking, and was able to suggest certain alternative medicines. Within two weeks Claire came off all prescription medication and was taking those suggested by Chris. That was such a brave thing for Claire to do and must have been immensely difficult. However, this was such a positive step forward and helped my work with her considerably. I set up a weekly appointment for Claire to visit me for spiritual counselling and healing. After a couple of weeks both mum and daughter joined my spiritual education classes.

Before each appointment HQ would wake me around three in the morning. He would speak to me mind to mind, and he would project visualisation on to my eyelids, to reinforce what he was saying. He explained we humans emit a frequency. The frequency comes from our mind. He said, 'As you think so you pulsate.' I was to think of a radio or television, which was both a transmitter and a receiver, and how they could be tuned in to a specific channel. Claire's way of thinking had tuned her in to a channel that was compatible with certain people who had died, but refused to pass over. Whilst not all people who are in this half way stage are bad people, unfortunately the people she tuned in to didn't have a nice way of thinking, and had very little empathy or compassion. HQ said 'like attracts like, or light attracts light'.

He said each thought had a vibration, and this vibration had a tone as well as a colour. For instance, negative thoughts would produce a darkish green colour. The more negative the thought, the darker the colour. We can see these thought colours in the aura. There was also a pitch associated with each colour, and the darker the colour, the more specific the pitch. HQ said 'Just because a person thinks negatively it doesn't mean they are a bad person, but bad people also think negatively. This is what I mean when I tell you "like attracts like, or light attracts light". Claire is a good person but her repeated way of thinking has brought her to a vibration that is occupied by people who are not so good'.

I then heard a static noise in my ear and I saw streaks of lightening on my eyelids. I said to HQ 'I know that noise, I have heard it repeatedly. When I was feeling so irritable and couldn't be around people that noise was with me constantly. I even had my hearing tested because of it. It's still not gone completely, but it's almost gone. What does it mean?' He told me 'Your way of thinking was changing; you were off channel for a while. You have grown so much that you no longer occupy the same frequency. You were not gelling with the people around you as you were off frequency, but you are almost tuned in properly now'. I was absolutely incredulous. What I was being told was astounding, and yet it made perfect sense to me. HQ said 'You are so much easier for me to work with now, as you are thinking and acting in a more balanced way'.

He told me that when I worked with Claire I had to concentrate on changing what was in her subconscious mind. He said Claire was extremely sensitive and her problems had been compounded by her musical gift. He reminded me that every sound or tone had a frequency. HQ said when Claire was born her thought waves were very light, and spirit workers could easily influence her, as they can with most children. Once she went to school and started to interact with other children, insecurity crept in to her way of thinking. Claire's pulsation had emitted that insecurity. Some of the children sensed this by picking up on that frequency and, as children will, they used this as a weapon against Claire.

Claire was a very different child. She lived a lot in her head, thinking and humming away to herself. Our society very often doesn't like 'different', and so Claire was not popular at school. Over the years she developed a poor self-image. Her thoughts became more and more negative and she emitted a low pulsation. Eventually, through her thoughts, she connected with a channel that was just the right frequency to allow her to resonate with it. Imagine she was a musical instrument and a tuning fork was tuning her in to resonate with the other instruments. Once she reached that channel, she found it impossible to come off it. She was blending with the orchestra perfectly, and the music they were making was menacing and dark.

It was my job to help her get off this channel. I had to tell her how valuable she was as a person, and emphasise what wonderful potential she had to express herself through her music. I also had to reinforce to her that her experiences could be changed from a negative to a positive. She needed to understand that there must be thousands of people like her in the world, and she could be such a help to them. I also had to give her a spiritual education, so that she could understand about life.

However, HQ would stress to me 'Yvonne, remember, you must help but not carry. It is Claire who must do the hard work needed to change her frequency. You have to tell her

"No pain, no gain". She has to break through the pain barrier, and only she can do it.' After about four weeks of working with Claire she started to feel happier and said the voices were not as loud. I was ecstatic, thinking she had cracked it, but HQ showed me differently. He woke me up around three on the morning of Claire's next appointment and he said 'Claire is made of straw and one blow can flatten her.' On my eyelids I saw my flipchart, and in the middle there was drawn a round shape. At the sides of the shape were slightly curvy lines.

HQ said 'Imagine Claire is an island in the middle of the sea, and the water is virtually flat. The flatness is Claire's thought waves. Someone can easily swim to her. The swimmers are the negative voices communicating with Claire.' He went on to say, 'Then imagine larger waves coming from the island, those larger waves are Claire's happy thoughts. These thoughts will push the swimmers back. Claire is not yet strong enough to sustain those larger waves. An unkind word from someone, or a bad look directed at her, will take away her new found vibrancy. The swimmers can then swim back to the island.'

I asked, 'Well what should I do?', and he said 'Keep working to change what's in the database of her mind, as she has to change her view of herself and of life. Tell her about people and the frailties you are born with. Reinforce these frailties are in every one of you. Let her know she is equally capable of directing an unkind word or look at someone. She must be strong enough to withstand this when it is directed at her, because it is part of life.'

I asked HQ, 'If she succeeds in changing what's deep in her mind, what about those times in the future when she gets depressed or has a bad experience, as we all do?' He replied 'The core of Claire has to be strong. She needs to be like an island that is constantly surrounded by strong waves.

Then when the flatness comes in, it will be opposed by the stronger waves and will be buffeted and moved along. Again I repeat, the core of Claire needs to be strong. It is part of your job to help her become positive in her outlook and love herself. She must know her worth, but remember Yvonne, you do not carry'.

After about twelve weeks, because Claire was so much better, her parents Bryan and Ann took her on holiday to America, and this would be the real test. How would she cope when she was away? HQ told me I had to 'cut', as I was starting to feel anxious about her. So I did, I made myself stop thinking of her and carried on with my work.

Claire had been away for four weeks, and when she came back from America she looked wonderful. She radiated happiness. HQ had woken me early that morning and told me there was to be no more healing, and the counselling was to be set for once a fortnight. He said 'Claire is ready to stand on her own two feet, she has altered her frequency and there is only Claire now in her head. You must tell her she is ready to go it alone. It will be up to her to say when she feels confident enough to stop the counselling altogether, as Claire is now in control of Claire.' I saw Claire for one more counselling session, and then she said she was strong enough to stand alone. I was so proud of her at that moment. She had been through hell, and now she was back. I was privileged to have worked with her.

Through working with Claire I now understood so much more about the aura. I am able to see people's auras, that gossamer pulsation surrounding us, and sometimes I see the colour within. I can use the colour as a diagnostic tool, and know if their thoughts are emotionally balanced, depressed, negative, and happy and so on.

I now understand that when we close our eyes and see colours on the eyelids we are seeing with our third eye the vibration or frequencies that we transmit and receive. Red would mean emotional imbalance, dark green or a dirty green is negativity, blue is depression. We need to visualise white when we see these colours, as white is balance. We should all try to think in a more balanced way. Light green or lime green means working with the mind, yellow is positivity, orange is wisdom and violet and purple are the connection with spirit. This connection is at its strongest when we are balanced. It is when we achieve this balanced state we can work with spirit most efficiently, as we are on their channel or vibration.

I think back to the dream HQ gave me, showing I was wearing a puzzle and it is all so clear to me now. The puzzle is the aura or the frequency we emit, and this attracts other frequencies to us. We are all instruments blending with other instruments. Some of us make beautiful music, while others are out of tune.

If you would like to learn to see the aura you could practice on a friend. Stand the friend against a blank wall, a dark wall is best. Look at the top of your friend's head and keep staring, letting your eyes go off focus. You will begin to see a bright pencil outline around your friend. This pencil outline is the life force and it is different to the aura. Everything that has solidity has a life force, and the solidity is made up of atoms which are particles and waves. The waves cause a friction, and the friction gives off a magnetic impulse. This magnetic impulse is the life force. It is the life force that healers work on when they channel healing energy from spirit. If someone had a bad shoulder it would show in the life force. If healing energy were able to disperse what was in the life force then it would have an effect on the physical body and, hopefully, the shoulder would be healed.

Once you can see the life force, keep staring and in your peripheral vision you might see another, perhaps weird shape. It can be unevenly distributed around the head and shoulder area, and it can extend quite far out. This is the aura. Everything that has consciousness has an aura, and the aura comes from the mind of the spirit and is made up of thought waves or frequencies. Keep staring straight ahead as otherwise you won't retain the aura. Eventually through practice you might be able to see the colours within the aura.

A few days before Christmas 2003, I received a call from a young girl. She sounded very fragile and vulnerable, and she said 'Hello, my name is Susan. I've lost my baby and I wanted to come to see you'. I said 'Oh Susan, I am so sorry to hear that, don't tell me any more otherwise it will dilute the evidence but when did you want to come?' She said 'Can I see you before Christmas? I know there's only a few days left, but if I could come the day before Christmas Eve that would be great'. I agreed a time for the day she requested, and then she said 'The only problem is, my family don't want me to do this and my mum might want someone to come with me'. I said, 'Susan, I completely understand your family feeling this way. I would be exactly the same if I were in their shoes; what ever makes you feel good is fine by me.'

I took great care in preparing for Susan's visit, as I knew it was important that she get the best out of me. She was due in the middle of the afternoon, and so the day before I did all my housework and last minute rushing around. On the day, I had my main meal early, and then relaxed and waited for her.

I spoke to HQ in my mind and said, 'Please help me to help Susan; she needs to know about her baby. If there is anyone in your world that Susan knew and loved when they were on earth, please HQ, help them to come, and also help them to give me good, clear evidence of survival'. When Susan came she had her friend Rachel with her. Susan was about seventeen and was a very pretty girl. The sadness and hurt in her eyes was evident.

We sat in my lounge and exchanged brief pleasantries, I put the tape on and we began. 'Susan, your maternal grandmother is here, she tells me her name is Nancy. She knew you prayed for her help when your **daughter** was in the hospital, and she wants you to know she heard you. She is saying you were there when your girl died.' Susan interrupted and said 'Well no you see, this is one of my problems. I took her to the hospital and the nurse took her from me. I was told to wait, and she was taken through swing doors. Her little head turned, and she looked at me and held my gaze as she was taken through the doors, and then the doors closed. The next time I saw her she was on a life support machine. I don't know whether she was already dead, and they might have wired her up to the machine for my benefit. I can't bear it if I wasn't with her.' 'Susan, listen to what I am saying, your nana is saying you were with your girl when she died.'

Susan was still in shock over the death of her baby, you could see it in her face. She looked at me, and gave a passive little smile. 'Your nana is saying your girl breathed it in' and I drew a deep, slow breath. Again Susan interrupted 'Well this is another of my problems. She had meningitis and I was told she either came in to contact with a carrier, or it was in the air. I feel so guilty, and couldn't bear it if I had taken her somewhere and she became infected as a result of it.' 'Susan, nana is saying she breathed it in. It was in the air my darling. How can you be responsible for that? There are so many things of the air we cannot see. We never know what we are breathing in. Do you understand what I am saying, she breathed it in.' Rachel interrupted and said to Susan, 'You had two questions when we came here, and both have been answered, Sue.'

Nancy went on to tell Susan other important facts, and reassured Susan when her girl died Nancy was there to meet her, and she wrapped her in her arms and loved her. The reading took about forty-five minutes, and then the energy went. I told the girls I had all the time in the world, and they could stay for as long as they liked. I told Susan to ask me any questions, as I could answer them. And so we sat, it started to get dark, and I put candles around the room.

There was a wonderful sense of peace and Susan asked so many things, such as 'Where is my baby now?' I answered, 'This is the earth plane; we live a life on earth in the physical body. Your baby has come out of her body and she has gone to the astral plane and returned to her natural state, which is spirit. Think of her body as a car and her spirit as the driver. She has left the car and walked away leaving the car abandoned, but she still exists Susan.' She said 'Is my nana feeding her?' and I told her 'This is something we need when in the physical body, when we come out of the body we take our nourishment in a different way, we are fed by the energy we absorb.' She said 'Is she happy?' and I told her 'Absolutely, in the world of spirit they don't have the frailties we humans have like hate, greed and jealousy. They live without these weaknesses. Think of how wonderful that must be'.

She wanted to know, 'Can she see me, and does she know I love her?' I said, 'As you know, your nana was waiting for your girl when she died, and she took her to the astral plane. Once there your girl has to go through a process. Firstly she is given healing. She is like the battery of a car, and she will need to be topped up with energy. She will then go through a process of having her mind unlocked; everything that has gone before, and I am talking about past lives, and what she came here to achieve will be known to her. Once she has gone through that process and has the full power of the mind, she can then come back and forth to you.

She probably won't stand solid in front of you, as that takes such a lot of planning and energy from the spirit side, but she can communicate she is around you in cryptic and subtle ways. She can easily interfere with the electrics, such as turning the television on and off, or changing channels, distortion on the screen, and that type of thing. She can put thoughts in your mind, or perhaps move an object, she can also influence coincidence. Even a smell that you associate with her can come back to you strongly. Also, she can come to you in your sleep state, and you might dream of her, or you could get a symbol that's representative of her. She can feel all your emotion and as much as you love her, she loves you. She will want for you to be happy and get on with your life, as she will be getting on with her life in the spirit world.'

She said 'Why did she have to die?', and I told her 'Nothing in this life is guaranteed, and we are all vulnerable to outside influence. Just know if it wasn't her time to go, whatever she came here to learn, she can learn on the astral plane. It could be she was only meant to be with you a brief time, and what she needed to learn could only be achieved on the astral plane. Life is like a huge tapestry, and your girl's death will have taught you something as well'. Finally she asked, 'Will I ever see her again?' and I told her 'Just as your nana was there to meet your girl when she died, so your girl will be there to meet you when you die. We all have a welcoming committee to meet us. Don't ever think of ending your life Susan, because you have a lot to do and achieve on earth, but when it is your time to go, just know she will be there waiting for you. In the meantime, get on with living your life and know that your girl is living hers.'

All the time this conversation was taking place, I would constantly ask her if she understood what I was saying. When she didn't, I would explain it to her in another way. There were big, comfortable silences, and the three of us would just sit quietly. I could imagine Susan's mind working, absorbing and processing what I had told her. Now and then I could see the lime green that was coming through in her aura, and the red that was heavily present was starting to lessen.

Eventually, after more than three hours, Susan thanked me and said she felt so different. Rachel said 'When I came here I was very sceptical and a bit worried for Susan, but you've convinced me. I am now a believer'. The girls said a few words to one and other that I couldn't hear, and Rachel hugged Susan. I asked 'What did you say?' and Rachel said, 'When we leave here I am going to meet a gang of our friends. We are having a drink and a meal to celebrate Christmas. Susan now feels able to join us'. I couldn't have been given a better Christmas present; I was so pleased to hear that.

When sitting with people such as Susan, I don't cry or show any emotion, although I do empathise with them and I am quite tactile. I now help people to help themselves by arming them with knowledge, and working with them to become positive. The old Yvonne couldn't have done this. She would have felt so sorry for their problems, jumped in feet first, carrying and taking away their responsibility. I am thrilled to say I have come a long way.

One day a man came to see me. I didn't know why he had come, but I said, 'Your father is here with us, and he's holding a young man by the hand. The young man seems to have some kind of mental disability, and your father is holding his hand tightly, and their arms are up in the air, punching the air as though in triumph.' The man was so pleased to hear this, and I asked him what it meant.

He said the young man was his brother. In life he had been a schizophrenic, and he had killed himself a couple of years before. Their father had just died and the mother was in bits,

218

frightened that her husband and son wouldn't be together in death, as she was thinking on religious lines. She thought her son had two strikes against him. Firstly, he had never been christened, and secondly, he had taken his own life.

I reminded the man that in the Bible it spoke of God's mansion having many rooms, and I told him symbolically this meant there was room for the unexpected visitor, those people who passed before their time; no one was turned away. I told the man to play the tape to his mother so she could hear for herself. Her husband and son were together, and they seemed very, very happy to me.

A young girl came for a reading. Her name was Alisha and she was from Swansea. Her lovely twenty-one year old sister had just been killed in a car accident. Alisha was desolate.

Apparently a couple of weeks before her sister was killed she was on her PC and found her way to my web site. She told Alisha she was going to visit me, and she did visit, but not in the flesh. She made contact immediately and gave her nickname of RahRah. She told Alisha she was fine and her passing had been easy. She said their father, who had died years before, was there to meet her. RahRah spoke of their mother and her devastation, and as evidence she said things that had happened since her passing. RahRah then spoke about a young girl known to both sisters, who had died a year before. She said she'd met up with her in the spirit world.

After the reading Alisha said 'Yve, I don't understand RahRah mentioning our friend because we are one religion and our friend was a different religion. How can she be where RahRah is?' I told her 'Alisha, I can only tell you I have connected with many, many people who have died, and they have been from all different religions and beliefs. They are all in the same place.'

219

Another lovely lady who came for a reading was called Cath. She was desolate as her wonderful daughter Lynette had killed herself three years before. Cath had never had a reading before but she came because of the strange happenings in her home. In Cath's bedroom she had two shelves on the wall. Articles of Lynette's were placed on the shelves and, for no apparent reason, these articles kept falling off. Cath assured me the shelves were stout, and securely placed, with plenty of room to hold the things that were placed there. There was no explanation she could think of for these things to happen.

I asked Cath 'Has Lynette's death been so awful for you to face that you have put her "on a shelf" and blocked her from your mind?' Poor Cath admitted 'I have had to. When Lynette did that terrible thing I had a heart attack. I was only forty-five then. Since that time I cannot think of my daughter as my heart beats violently and I go in to a panic.' I told Cath, 'Symbolically your bedroom represents what is around you in life. Lynette is saying "Mum, I am around you, I have survived. Please take me off the shelf." Lynette loves you and has your best interest at heart; she wants you to stop hurting.'

We sat and chatted for about an hour and Cath explored her feelings. She did a lot of crying in that hour, but when she was leaving she hugged me and said 'I am going to think of Lynette every day. I will give myself a couple of minutes a day to start off with and then, once my confidence is back, perhaps I can let her in a little more.' I was so happy to hear that.

In January 2004 I got a call from our local newspaper, the South Wales Echo. A lady introduced herself as Alison Stokes, Head of Features Content. She was looking for someone like me to run a weekly column, answering reader's queries about spiritual matters. I told Ali I could do so much more than that, and I explained about symbols. The result was in March 2004 my column began. Readers send me their dreams to be analysed, they ask for explanations regarding spiritual happenings, and they want to know about life after death. I am enjoying this work so much and I love the fact I can share my knowledge with a wider audience.

Eight

Acknowledging earth angels

Catching up with Elizabeth and acknowledging the many, many earth angels.

The last pages of my book I would like to devote to Elizabeth, the wonderful lady I told you about earlier. You will remember she was married to Joseph, and their daughter Maureen died leaving three little children, and one of them was only three weeks old!

Elizabeth is now eighty-one, and since Joseph's death almost ten years ago, she has lived on her own. Despite her horrendous grief and suffering ill health, she has been very active in helping Maureen's children to grow. We keep in touch from time to time and I rang Elizabeth and told her about my book and asked if I could have an update for the readers. I went to her house with a tape recorder and we sat and chatted. Following is a transcript of our conversation.

I said, 'Elizabeth, I'm writing a book about my life and spiritual work. Part of my story is about the healing clinic at my former home, and you and Joseph were such a big part of that. I have printed off what I have written about you both and I will leave it for you to read later. Do you think you're up to it?' Elizabeth said 'I am love, don't worry about that and it's nice of you to include us, but I'm sure people will find us boring'. I said 'How could anyone ever find you boring? You are such a brave and wonderful lady, and I want the whole world to know about you.'

'Would you give me an update on your situation, and perhaps you could look back and just tell me your thoughts'. Elizabeth said 'I would like to do that Yvonne, but if I ramble on you will stop me love won't you?' I said 'I will Elizabeth, don't worry about that'.

Elizabeth said 'I miss Joseph terribly; he was such a good man. He worked as a tailor and when he got home from work, he would roll his sleeves up and get stuck in with the chores. He used to take in alterations to supplement our income and he would sit with his sewing machine whirring away, chatting with the kids and finding out about their day. He had so much time to give everyone. When I look back I can't believe how our lives changed so drastically when Maureen died. It's like everything before was someone else's happy life'.

'I remember everything about the healing clinic at your house. I originally took Joseph there through meeting a man called Dave who came to repair our television aerial. Dave said to Joseph "You're not feeling very well are you?" and Joseph said he wasn't. We came ostensibly for Joseph, but later it was me that needed the healing.'

'We just knocked on your door didn't we? What a cheek we had. It was always such a comforting place to be and there was a lovely, lovely atmosphere there. The coffee always seemed extra special, and Joseph loved going there. He wasn't a social person at all. He would rather stay at home but he always wanted to go to you, always.'

'I remember in the winter you would make sure the house was warm for the people who were ill. You would have the heating on and gas fires burning and yet Joseph would still feel cold. You used to have a hot water bottle ready for him, so he could hold it to him. He loved that. I was sixty-nine then and he was seventy-one. Maureen was pregnant with her third baby'.

'When Maureen died we were plunged into hell. After her funeral I remember being in the crematorium and looking at Maureen's coffin, and she was standing at the side of it in her coat and was waving to me. I am telling you I saw her as clear as clear as day. I still have the coat she was wearing. I leave it hung in the hall. I like to pretend she's visiting me and has hung her coat there. Maureen's husband and the kids needed so much looking after and Joseph and I were getting old, and he was so ill with his Parkinson's disease'.

'After six weeks my son-in-law employed a nanny who was properly trained. The new baby needed constant care, and she was only just two months old by then. I had the three kids every Saturday while my son-in-law was working, and every Thursday night so he could attend counselling for his grief.'

'I remember the first time I decided I couldn't go on grieving with such intensity. I had the children with me and we were sitting in the conservatory. The middle child was kneeling on the floor and she turned her head and I saw Maureen on her face, it was so clear. I saw that and thought, "I can't go on like this; I have to pull myself together and carry on for these children. I have to find the strength to nurture them". We were all so traumatised. How can you expect little children to understand their mummy has gone and won't be back? They were crying for her constantly. I accepted I had to be there for them and it was a challenge. I would help Maureen by helping her children. It was all so very, very hard and I was trying to look after Joseph as well, as he had taken to bed'.

'There have been moments when I have been absolutely desperate and didn't know which way to turn, and I have asked her and she has always given me answers. Many, many times I have been distraught. I remember once being in the car and stopping it and starting screaming. I was screaming at the top of my voice because I didn't know what else to do. She was such a beautiful girl, she was lovely, she was full of fun and we were so close to each other. It should never, ever have happened'.

'I miss Joseph a lot and I feel him around me all the time. When I go to bed I put the bedside light on and it goes blink, blink, and blink. I have checked to see if there is anything wrong with it and there's not. It's just that one light next to me; isn't that strange?'

'In the early days of Joseph's death my doctor booked for me to see a counsellor. I said to her, "I feel awful because I haven't grieved for my husband at all but I know he will understand why". She said "Next time you come bring something that belonged to him". I forgot this until the last moment. It came in to my mind as I was leaving for the appointment.'

'I rushed in to the kitchen and Joseph was always worried someone would cut themselves on carving knives and such like, when they were looking in the cutlery draw. He made leather sheaves on the sewing machine to cover the knives. I got two of those out and a sanding disc because he loved smooth wood. His hobby was carpentry. I took them to the lady and she said "Arrange them as you want" and so I automatically laid a table. The disc was the plate, and the two sheaves were the knives and forks. The minute I did that he walked in to the room, I know he did. The feeling of him, his presence, it was just fascinating. The lady said it was wonderful for me, but he definitely came to me. When I really, really need him he always comes. Every morning when I wake up he's in the bed. Sometimes I think "Move over", forgetting he's dead'.

'I used to pick up the kids on a Saturday morning and one day my son-in-law's father was there. He had lost his wife quite recently and I used to give him a lift back home. The kids would pile into my car with their night clothes on, and get dressed at my house. One day the father said to me "Could you drop me at the crematorium gates?" and I told him "Yes". I turned in there to drop him off, and the children were all in the back and they were saying "Yippee we are going to see mummy", and I said "You can't go out there in your night clothes" and they said "Of course we can, race you to Mummy's stone", and I will never forget the sight of three little ones racing in their pyjamas and dressing gowns to see a stone where their mummy was lying. That was seven years ago. It was so touching'.

'The kids sense her around them all the time. The middle child told me she feels mummy there but she has to be alone to feel her. She sits in the lounge on a chair and she feels her come to her and feels her presence.'

'Another funny thing happened in the car. We were driving along one day and they were making a lot of noise. I said "Please be quiet its dangerous when someone's driving," One of the girls said "Like Princess Diana?" and I said "Yes". She said "Do you think she's with mummy now?" and I said "Yes she is, darling". She said, "She's probably deciding what colour lipstick to put on", I thought that was lovely. That was about six years ago'.

'They have changed now as the two eldest have gone into secondary school, and their lives change when they go there, they become so independent. Before that they were very, very close to me and their mother. I still have the youngest a lot as she is only eleven.'

'One day last summer I had been visiting the children and we had a lovely time together. I started to drive home, but half way there I felt I needed to go back. I turned the car around and drove back, and I sat on the couch with the kids, and the girls were cuddled up to me and their brother was on a chair. I told them I wanted to be near them, I said "It must have been your mummy telling me to cuddle you," and we had a lovely two hours of reminiscing. They love hearing stories about their mummy when she was little, they devour them and I could see the happiness on their face, it was absolutely wonderful'.

'I feel I've had to stay on earth to do a job of work. Two years ago, in February 2003, I had breast cancer and had my two breasts off. I told my surgeon he couldn't let me die as I had three children to help care for, and needed just a few more years. I now have internal bleeding and the doctor can't find where I am bleeding from, but I am hanging on in there. I believe I am being kept alive for the sake of the children. I know I am a great support to the kids, when they have any little problems they always ring and tell me.

Elizabeth stopped talking and I said 'Elizabeth you have done the most wonderful job for your daughter. When it's your time to go, the instant you die you will come out of the body and Joseph and Maureen will be waiting for you. Can you imagine what Maureen will say to you? She'll say you have done over and above anything that could have been asked of you. My HQ always tells me "No pain, no gain", and my former teacher Joyce always says "For every good deed we do on earth we earn a tick, and each tick turns into a brick". You will be able to build a mansion with your bricks when you go over Elizabeth '.

Just as I finished speaking we heard a lady's voice calling 'Hello', and there was a knocking on the door. Elizabeth said to me 'It's Sue, Maureen's friend'.

When Sue came in Elizabeth introduced us and told Sue I was a spiritual medium. Sue said 'Are you the lady that ran the healing centre?' and I told her I was. She then said, 'Well what a coincidence, I was talking to my brother and telling him about my friend who died years ago. Before he died he was in such terrible pain and I used to take him to a place in Park Grove, in Cardiff where a tall, older man called John would give him healing. I have just left my brother after having that conversation, going down memory lane and now here is the healing lady'.

I said to Elizabeth, 'Sue is talking about the John who used to heal at the clinic and was in charge of the trainees working there. Do you remember him Elizabeth? He's a very nice-looking man, very smart and he holds himself well. He is married to my former teacher Joyce.' Sue said, 'I've only called in on an impulse and didn't know you had a visitor Elizabeth'. Elizabeth said, 'Yvonne is writing a book and she's devoting her last pages to me Sue, although I don't know what I've done to deserve that. We were just talking about Maureen and I was going over these years without her'.

Sue said, 'I couldn't believe it when she died and was in disbelief. When I would visit the house to see the kids I was always very aware of Maureen there, you could feel her presence. Sometimes driving past her house I would look up at the bedroom window and you could see her tartan dressing gown hanging on the back of the door. Her husband's sister took it away, but now recently the eldest girl is wearing it, so his sister kept it to give to one of the kids when they were grown enough'.

Elizabeth said, 'Maureen had that dressing gown for Christmas just before she died and it was gorgeous. I went one day and one of the girls was wearing this dressing gown but I didn't know it was Maureen's and I said to her 'You look lovely darling' and she proudly said 'This is mummy's'.

Sue explained she worked as a teacher, and she was a teacher at the school Maureen's children attended. 'The eldest child had only been in the school a term, and then the middle child came to school as well. My two children and Maureen's two eldest were all friends together. I was still teaching there off and on when the youngest joined the school. I used to do anything I could to help them'.

Elizabeth said 'I remember once going to the school and feeling such an outsider. All the mothers turned to look at me and Sue stepped out of the door, came towards me with her arms open and gave me a big hug. I will never forget that gesture. People didn't know how to react because of the tragedy around me and Sue was such a support'.

It was time for me to go and I gave Elizabeth a kiss and left her with Sue. In the car coming home I thought of Sue's arrival and the conversation she had with her brother, and I knew it was no coincidence. I believe Maureen wanted Sue's kindness acknowledged in my book, and she influenced Sue to call at Elizabeth's so we could meet. That wasn't all. John was the tutor for the healers working at the clinic at my old home, and he and the healers had helped Elizabeth and Joseph and all the healers needed to be acknowledged. Also, Joyce was John's wife and her invaluable contribution to spiritual education and development needed to be acknowledged. I am happy to do this small service for Maureen and acknowledge all of the earth angels, as I am a spiritual medium, and I'm in service to the universe.